POINTS

OF

LIGHT

26 POINTS OF LIGHT

ILLUMINATING ONE CANCER SURVIVOR'S JOURNEY
FROM DIAGNOSIS TO REMISSION

MAUREEN O'BRIEN

Based on one woman's personal story of the diagnosis of Stage IV Lymphoma.
Cataloging-in-Publication data is available.

Stock images by Vecteezy.com and Unsplash.com.

ISBN 978-1-7349590-1-7
Printed in the United States of America
First Printing: 2021
25 24 23 22 21   5 4 3 2 1

To order, visit www.globalwlf.com
Publisher: Batavia Press

This book is dedicated to all those who carried me when I could not carry myself and to those who are carrying another right now. Some of these bright lights are identified in the next pages. I am forever grateful.

It is also dedicated to all those impacted by a diagnosis that they will receive today.

I pray this book offers you help, hope, and light.

CONTENTS

FOREWORD

Sean Michael Gallagher
Part of Another's Community of Care

When Maureen first contacted me to ask if I would consider writing the foreword for this book, I was honored and a little scared. She found my story in my best friend's book, *Fear Is a Choice*. My best friend is James Conner, running back for the Pittsburgh Steelers. I played a small role in his story, but Maureen saw it differently. She and I instantly connected on such a powerful and personal level. We met virtually over Zoom, and we quickly learned much about each other's stories. I knew I had to be part of this project. Her vision to help others when all hope seems lost spoke to me. To be able to dig deep inside yourself, to find the inner strength you wondered if you had, is something I know a little bit about.

She asked me to share my experience in dealing with the traumatic events in my life, most specifically cancer. She wanted to know how I overcame the adversity and how I was able to support my closest friend and family. She wondered how I stayed upright. I knew I had to be involved with this project because frankly, I had not seen anything like this before—something representing the multitude of voices of those people surrounding the person at the center of a diagnosis. I realized how helpful a tool like this would have been for me as my younger self.

I spent weeks staring at a blank page trying to find the right words to write. I have told my story so many times. Putting it down on paper in my own words seemed different. I didn't know where to start, or if people would have any desire to read my story. I'm not a victim of some great tragedy. I haven't battled cancer myself, but I have witnessed many great battles. I know the feeling of helplessness while watching someone that you love fight for their life.

My life has been driven by three major things. First is faith. Second is family. Third is football. Perhaps you think the first two are universal. Maybe, but I believe the difference is that most people do not live what they say.

When I was growing up, things weren't easy for my five siblings and me. My dad was a lifelong sportscaster for a small local market. For as long as I can remember, I would stay by his side so that I might get a chance to be on the sidelines for high school and local college football games. I learned at a very young age that in the game of football, just as in life, it's about getting up every single time you're knocked down and moving forward, no matter how deep the mud or the mess in which you might find yourself.

After two years of playing tackle football, one of the game days landed on my twelfth birthday. The day that was supposed to be all about me. It was a Saturday afternoon. Football games were going on everywhere at every level, including at Edinboro University, where we would often spend a good number of our days. Dad was Edinboro's photographer. That day, I couldn't care less about Edinboro. I only cared about my game and my birthday.

We were at Edinboro two hours before my game started, and by the end of the first half, Edinboro was leading 14–7. My dad was focused on doing his thing. Click. Click. Click. He seemed to think that his role as photographer was something I cared about that day. The reality: it was just nice to be a kid on the sideline at a college football game.

As the players made their way to the locker room, it was time for me to leave for my game. Not only was it my birthday, but I was the star running back and linebacker. When we left for the game, my dad stayed behind to do his job. I knew that when that game was over, he would show up on my sideline. Since it was my birthday, I expected a lot of family to be on the sideline. Of course, my mom would be there.

The weather was awful. As my coach pulled us together in the pouring rain, he told us that all our attention had to be focused on the field, and that this opponent would be the toughest one we faced so far.

The toughest opponent I would face. If only . . .

As we broke the huddle, I remember Coach screaming, "Gallagher, you need to make a play!" I remembered those words long after that game.

We lined up. As I always did, I looked to the sideline. No Mom. No Dad. For whatever reason, I was alone. And as the whistle blew, none of the people that I thought really mattered were on the sidelines. In my world, they were all I needed.

What I didn't realize was that events outside of that football field were still going on as if this game did not matter.

My team did not have a runaway victory, but we did win. Two touchdowns were scored by me, the birthday boy.

You're probably wondering what this story has to do with being impacted by a traumatic event. Following the game, the team came back to my house for a birthday sleepover. My mother left the house to get a birthday cake. Cruel twist: she did not return. She had not been in an accident or anything; she just decided on her own. There we were, twelve of my closest friends, sitting around, all wondering if or when we were going to have cake and blow out candles. It never happened. No cake, no candles. My mom just decided she didn't want to be with us anymore. She did not come back.

How does a twelve-year-old boy handle this? I decided I would handle it the same way I played the game of football. I. Would. Get. Back. Up. I kept hearing, "Gallagher, you need to make a play!"

When you get knocked down, you must get up. This time, however, the rest of my family and my friends had to help pick me up.

Family doesn't always look the way people may think it should. I deliberately distanced myself from my mom's side of the family. My friends became the family that I got to choose, and I knew they would choose me. This gave me some feeling of control. My friends showed up every day, not realizing they were helping me through the darkest days of my life. I grew extra close to their families, even spending holidays with them. They became my community of care because they made the decision to be present to me in any way they could.

Just like in football, we set up a plan. We had plays that we would execute. But even with the best playbook, sometimes things happen outside of the plan. My dad was diagnosed with kidney disease, and shortly after, his job was eliminated. I remember sitting in my room staring out the window. How much more would I be required to endure?

We were going to lose our house. I felt mortified. When the sheriff came to post the notice, he turned around and said to me, "Son, as soon as I leave, take that notice down. I'm certain I won't know you have removed it." The sheriff did not know it, but at that moment, he became part of my own community of care.

I did not blame my mom for leaving us. I just had to come to terms with my circumstances. I was content with who I was becoming as a person, and especially who I was on the field, because that field was the one place where all was right with the world. I realized that we don't always get to choose what happens to us in life, but we do get to choose how we respond.

I went on to play college football at Edinboro. My dad was still taking pictures of every move we made. My best friend James went on to play for the University of Pittsburgh. My mom eventually came back into my life. Every time I looked up in the stands, she was right there waving her Edinboro pennant. Things started to feel as though perhaps they would be normal. And then it happened. I would be tested again.

As the season went on, I became much closer with my friends and family. Mom was even coming to all the games and staying after to tell me she was proud of me. I looked for her at every game, but one Saturday afternoon, when I looked over at the sidelines, I saw just my sister. With her eyes down, she shook her head. I knew that Mom was not coming. I thought maybe something came up . . . but it didn't seem right.

Later that night, when I was out with some of the other players, I got a text from my mom: "Sean, I am in the hospital. I am not feeling well. I'm so sorry I missed your game."

I asked if everything was all right. After a few minutes, I received her response. "No, Sean, things are not all right. I have a brain tumor."

As I read those words on my screen, I dropped the phone to the ground. My mind was spinning. I wanted to go to her, but I knew that I couldn't. I spent most of that night drinking in my room by myself. With my headphones on, I looked up facts about brain tumors. And when I arrived at the hospital the next day, just seeing her lying in the bed was too much for me. I broke down.

I wanted someone to tell me what I was supposed to do. I was lost in my head. Again, I could hear, "Make a play, Gallagher!" But what play could I make? I decided I would drive from school to the hospital every day until she was released. I wasn't going to lose her again.

My life now was about playing football, going to class, and driving back home to see my mom every chance I had. While in school, I worked hard to get good grades and help my team win. My goal was to become a movie producer. I longed to be someone who uses the big screen to tell stories that matter.

I did not return to the field for my sophomore season, because my mom lost her ten-month battle with brain cancer on the morning of September 9, 2014. She was a fighter to the end. In her final minutes, she was surrounded by family and love. I had to be strong, but I wasn't sure how to be strong. It seemed like we had just connected, and she was gone. I had wasted too much time. I was tearing myself to pieces over guilt and self-pity. I couldn't let my younger brothers see me. I hid in a closet, turned my phone off, and cried.

I had an exam that afternoon, and I knew my mom would want me to perform well. I muscled up and pulled myself together. Like in football, sometimes you're hurt or sick, but you only get a few opportunities to play. I knew I had to go to class and show everyone I could be strong. "Make a play, Gallagher!"

At the same time, my closest friend, James Conner, was coming into his own glory at the University of Pittsburgh. He would invite our entire family to every game. He said he loved giving us a place to escape from reality for a few short hours to watch him play. Watching him be so successful in a game that we previously shared created the respite that I needed. We traveled all over to watch him play. No one was a bigger fan than me. And my faith grew stronger during this time. Somehow, I just trusted that everything was going to work out. My dad's health had stabilized. My family was strong. Together, we would make it through.

James and I were home for Thanksgiving break. We decided to see the movie *Creed*, from the Rocky series. Prior to the movie, I could tell something was off with James. He didn't quite look like himself. His face was swollen. He looked like he hadn't slept in weeks. He said he had been sleeping on the couch. He told me he had visited the ear, nose, and throat doctor but hadn't yet heard back. I didn't think much of it at the time. In the movie, Rocky is diagnosed with cancer. As I watched, I saw that James was more emotionally attached to this movie than I would have expected. When the movie was over, my brother

Jack and I went to the mall, and James headed home. While sitting in the mall parking lot, my phone rang. It was James.

"Sean, I have something to tell you, I'm sick . . . I have cancer."

I could not believe what I was hearing. Punching the steering wheel, I erupted into tears. My brother was staring at me, scared. When I told him the news, he stared out the window. He did not respond. He was in shock.

I said out loud, "No. Not again. I will not lose anyone else in my life." And then I committed. "Make a play, Gallagher!" I would be the leader of his essential frontline!

James was supposed to be Superman; he was the best of us. Healthy, good-hearted, and supportive, he was always first in line to help someone else. I was tormented with worry about him. I drove James from Erie to Pittsburgh to go to his doctor. That drive felt like the longest drive of my entire life. James asked me about chemo and its effects on my mom. Holding back tears and knowing how beat up my mom got by the chemo, I promised him I wouldn't let him go through this alone. He would beat this. *We* would beat this. He just needed someone to remind him and encourage him. I would do that in any way I could.

Being part of another's community of care means showing up. That's what you've got to do first. Just show up. We spent time on the couch not even talking to each other, but he knew I was there. Sometimes that's the best thing you can do. You don't need to always have the right words to say.

As the quarterback of this team of caregivers, it was my job to hand the ball off to James. I couldn't run a linebacker over or stiff-arm a safety for him, but I knew it was my job to make life as easy as possible for James. And . . . I knew I couldn't fight that fight for him. Standing with his mother, his four brothers, and his teammates (who were also part of his community of care), I would show up to every appointment. Even if all we did was sit in silence and all I could offer was his barf bag (sorry for the graphic detail), that would be enough. I would never let him think he was alone in this fight.

James would go on to kick cancer's butt because he *believed* he could. Belief is critical from everyone on the team. Our job is to secure the belief in the person with the diagnosis that the treatment will work. It's our job to help them believe that their next title will be that of *survivor*.

James is a survivor. He went on to be drafted in the third round of the NFL draft by the Pittsburgh Steelers. He was selected for the 2018 Pro Bowl in just his second season.

I'm proud of my role as a leader of an essential community of care. I'm working as a photographer/videographer just like my dad. On Sundays, you'll find me on the sidelines for the NFL or at the Macomb Fieldhouse taking pictures for Edinboro University.

I want to encourage you both as a survivor and as part of a community of care. While I have not had a diagnosis of cancer personally, I believe I have been a survivor of some pretty tough circumstances. All of them prepared me to hold the sacred and honorable role as a leader on an essential frontline for a loved one.

I now invite you to read the firsthand story of another family who, like mine, was impacted by cancer. From the bottom of my heart, I want to thank you for your willingness to be part of another's essential frontline. And hey, [insert your own name]: "You need to make a play!"

PREFACE

Maureen (MO) O'Brien
Diagnosis: Stage 4 Diffuse Large B-Cell Non-Hodgkin's Lymphoma

Everything was great. We were getting ready to welcome a new year, 2016. All was falling into place. Finally. My four children were grown and self-sufficient. My husband and I had purchased a second home in Florida. We had great plans of wintering there to get out of the brutal Illinois cold and gray. We daydreamed about drinking frozen rum runners after long days on the beach. My business was soaring. I felt like I had everything.

What I did not know was . . . I also had cancer.

In December, I had a sinus infection that I could not shake. But it was December—I always had a sinus infection in December. We were on vacation with our youngest child, Lizzy, in Florida. We had flown to Miami and were making the trek to Key West. I did not feel great, but I could and *would* fight my way through it.

I remember feeling cold all the time. Really cold. And we were in Florida. I wondered why I could not regulate my own body heat. I recall standing in a scalding shower and still not being able to feel warm. At one point, I thought to myself, *I wish I could replace my batteries.* If only that were a thing. Then, at night, I would have terrible sweats that would soak my pajamas and bedsheets. I concluded that my body was just fighting the sinus infection.

It was true: my body *was* fighting. But it wasn't a sinus infection. And I had no idea just what sort of fight I was in for.

In January, my left shoulder started to hurt, and then I could not lift my left arm. I diagnosed myself (because I *am* a mom of four, so I'm *basically* a doctor) with a torn rotator cuff (because I believe I *am* an athlete, albeit via the couch), and I graciously refused the suggestions of those around me that I see a doctor.

Let me stop here and give you a little background. This categorization of my refusal to see a doctor as "gracious" may be refuted by some of my family members. I grew up in an Irish-Catholic family. Unless you had a bone protruding from your skin or you were bleeding profusely, you just kept your head down and kept working. That is what I knew; that is what I understood. Why would I go to a doctor for some sniffles and an arm that didn't work? Ridiculous . . . except for the sweats.

I made the mistake of telling my sister Patricia, a nurse with a PhD, that I could not lift my left arm. She asked, as any good health professional would, if I had been exercising a lot. I really wanted to answer this question with what I thought was the right answer, but I decided to tell the truth. No. I'd had no additional, excessive, or intense exercise as a part of my daily routine. She insisted that if I was not back to 100 percent in a couple of days, I would see a doctor. She made me promise. Dammit. Irish. Catholic. Guilt.

A couple of weeks passed, and I still did not have use of my left arm. In addition, a lingering cough was now part of my repertoire. My husband Dan and I were flying home from Florida on a Southwest Airlines flight. He always chooses the window, I, the aisle. I made him swear not to make eye contact with the passengers still boarding so that we might keep that middle seat vacant. Unfortunately—though now we know it was really our good fortune—a woman in her thirties boarded the plane and asked kindly if the seat was taken. We said the seat was hers.

Eye roll.

After settling in her seat, she immediately began a conversation with Dan. Dan is a quiet guy. He is very laid back. If he were any more laid back, he would be in a coma. She asked where he was from, whether Florida was his home or if he was just visiting, and other standard introductory niceties—but it was what happened next that was so striking. She told a grueling story of how she had had a sinus infection that she could not kick. She had felt extremely tired and run down and finally surrendered to seeing a doctor. She had never expected that she had leukemia. She had completed her treatment and was now in remission.

No. No. No. No. No. That was *her* story, not *my* story. That's what I kept repeating to myself. But Dan was now convinced that I had something much more serious than a sinus infection and a torn rotator cuff. The relentless nagging to see a doctor began.

A couple more weeks went by, and I finally acquiesced and went to see an orthopedic surgeon. I explained to Dr. Grosskopf that I could not lift my arm and that I had self-diagnosed with a rotator cuff injury. He agreed that something was not right and decided that X-rays would be a good place to start. (Is it the access to X-rays that makes you a *real* doctor? I digress.)

Since nothing seemed obvious in the X-ray, he decided to give me a cortisone shot to reduce inflammation. It did nothing. The final resolve was to send me to physical therapy every day for two weeks to see if we could loosen my shoulder and gain mobility. Off I went.

The physical therapist did everything he could do to loosen my shoulder, but my arm still would not move. After five days, he suggested that I go back to the orthopedic surgeon and get an MRI. He was convinced I had a giant tear that would require a surgical response.

I was beyond frustrated. My business was booming, and *I did not have time* to recover from a surgery. I started my logical planning: It was January now. If I had to have rotator cuff surgery, I could be ready for it by July.

The MRI was scheduled for a couple of days later. Dan went with me to the MRI (which never happens because—if you couldn't tell by now—I am a pretty independent person). I had the MRI. And we hadn't even pulled into our driveway when my cell phone rang. It was the orthopedic surgeon's office, wondering if we could come back to the office that afternoon to discuss the results of the test. We agreed.

Dammit. I just knew they were going to try to sell me on having the surgery sooner than July. Maybe I could swing it by the end of May . . .

We made ourselves as comfortable as is possible in a doctor's office. We had been ushered back to an exam room, where we made small talk about where we might go for lunch after the visit. Dr. Grosskopf interrupted that conversation.

I noticed immediately that he was not smiling. He looked worn out, his brow furrowed. He began the conversation with such an odd first question. He asked, "Maureen, how healthy are you?"

Well, this is odd, I thought to myself, but I proudly answered, "Dr. Grosskopf, I'm very healthy. I walk every day. I lift weights three times a week. I am on no medication. I don't even take a vitamin." I beamed at him.

He hung his head. "Maureen, I'm very sorry to tell you this, but you do not have a torn rotator cuff. You have a giant tumor in your left shoulder, and you need to see an oncologist. Today."

A silence lowered onto the room just before the world started to spin. What was *happening*? Surely, I hadn't heard him correctly. I was prepared to battle putting off rotator cuff surgery, but this? This just didn't make sense. I looked over at Dan, who looked like a deer caught in the headlights. This. Was. Happening.

Dr. Grosskopf sent us immediately from his office to the Northwestern Medicine-Delnor Cancer Center. Northwestern is a building I had passed at least five times a week on my local travels. I always said a prayer as I passed it. The prayer was that I would never have to see the inside of that building. Now, here I was registering as a patient.

The next day, Dan and I met with Dr. Bayer, the middle-aged, bow-tied, larger-than-life (both literally and figuratively) Head of Oncology. As he studied the MRI, Dan and I sat quietly. Dr. Bayer prescribed a sequence of tests, one a day for the rest of the month, that would include a bone scan, a full-body CT scan, a mammogram, a deep bone biopsy, an ultrasound, a PET scan, and more labs. He was trying to determine what the cancer was and where it had come from; he did not believe it had originated in my shoulder.

On February 25, after reviewing all the tests, we met again with Dr. Bayer. He let me know that he had called in every favor owed to him, and I would be going into surgery for multiple issues that Friday night. The surgery would include inserting a port in my chest so that I could receive chemotherapy. He reiterated that I would be receiving an extensive amount of it. They would remove my lymph nodes so that they could stage my cancer, although he was pretty sure it was stage 4 . . . because there isn't a stage 5. I would also have a steel rod inserted from my right hip to my kneecap because the cancer was eating away at my femur, and if they did not secure it, a fracture was certain to come.

A deer in the headlights. That is exactly how I felt. Absolute confusion set in. I began to challenge him. He must have the wrong chart. We were worried about my shoulder, and now he was talking about my hip? That just could not be right.

That's when Dr. Bayer took my hand and looked at me with intensity. He let me know that my shoulder was now a secondary concern. My hip needed to be the priority because it was critical that I be mobile, able to walk, when receiving the chemotherapy treatments. He went on to tell me that I would need to fight. In fact, he squeezed my hand and made me promise that I. WOULD. FIGHT. It would make all the difference in the outcome.

In July 2021, I celebrated five years of remission, but when I look back over my arduous journey, there is a lot I do not remember from that blurry time. That is part of the reason for this book: to piece the event together in a way I felt I needed to. I reached out to 26 members of my community of care, each of whom could pick up the story where I left off. Each one of these points of light helps to complete the story.

It is my sincere hope that the 26 points of light you'll hear from throughout this book make an impact on your life. Whether you're a patient or part of another person's community of care, may these reflections and illuminations give you the wisdom, encouragement, and support you need to make it through a difficult time.

I have learned much in these last five years. First, I no longer take my health for granted. I remember my father saying that if you have your health, you have everything. I didn't really understand it then. I understand it now.

I also learned that each breath is a gift. Really. None of us knows how much time we have left, yet we spend so much time stressing over things that do not matter. I was the queen of this behavior. I could get irritated over nothing. I'd love to tell you that those days are completely over for me, but they're not. I'm still working on being mindful and appreciating every moment, letting go of the little stuff, but I'm much better at it now than I used to be.

Finally, I have learned that people, not stuff, make all the difference. Looking into the faces of my grandchildren helps me recognize this the most. I could have missed all this. I could have never known their laughter, their joy, their sense of wonder. Sometimes I feel so overwhelmed with gratitude I can hardly breathe. I remember back to the prayers and promises I made while lying in that hospital bed. I remember promising that if I were lucky enough to make it to the other side of this disease, I would live fully. I would worry less. I would cherish each moment. I would have an impact where I could.

Whether it's you or someone you love who is directly experiencing a diagnosis, this is my advice to you: Don't wait. Live now. Keep having an impact, and keep looking up! And when the days feel tough, do what I did when I had cancer: take it a half day at a time.

INTRODUCTION

Can you imagine what a cancer diagnosis does to a family? Perhaps you don't have to imagine. Perhaps you've lived it. Perhaps you're living it now.

Every cancer story is different. What is similar is the impact that cancer has, not just on the person receiving the diagnosis but on the people surrounding that person. The impact is much like that of a pebble being thrown into a pond. Sometimes, only the immediate circle is visible. Upon closer observation, however, it is evident that additional circles appear and are impacted. But this impact can be hard to grapple with, and it's not always clear how others in the circle are coping with the news or what they're really going through.

In some ways, I was lucky—that is, if the words *cancer* and *lucky* can reside in the same sentence. What I mean is, I had great support in family, in friends, and in the best health care available. I learned a lot from them. We learned a lot from each other.

In this book, you are going to witness firsthand the impact of my diagnosis on each of those 26 points of light. I consider all of them, no matter which circle they belonged to, to be my bright lights! They include my immediate family—my husband and four kids—my siblings, my dearest friends, my coworkers, and the health care professionals who cared for me in my diagnosis of stage 4 diffuse large B-cell non-Hodgkin's lymphoma.

Throughout the book, I will introduce you to each contributor as they shine their own unique light on the topic and offer suggestions for others facing this situation. This multitude of voices shows that there's no one correct way to navigate a cancer diagnosis; the experience is shared throughout the entire community. I intend for this book (and especially Britta's Guide to Quarterbacking a Loved One's Diagnosis, which you'll find in chapter 14) to help you and your community navigate this difficult situation and remind you that others have been through it before. You are not alone.

Following each piece, you will also find excerpts taken directly from my site on CaringBridge (https://www.caringbridge.org), a free platform where friends and family can stay connected through any health journey. CaringBridge is such a gift for any family with this need. For me, it ultimately became a space where I could write about my deepest feelings. It felt safe. My family and friends used it to stay connected, keep each other up to date on my care, and send love and positivity across the miles. It is my sincere hope that these unedited posts might extend you some help and solace and act as an example of how your own community of care might embark on this journey together.

Not long ago, my nephew Kevin sent me the book *Fear Is a Choice: Tackling Life's Challenges with Dignity, Faith, and Determination* by James Conner, a running back for the Pittsburgh Steelers. James is also a survivor of lymphoma. Pittsburgh is my hometown, and like most people who have ever lived there, I am a crazy Steelers Fan. As I read about James's journey, I cried a lot. Our storylines are similar. However, I was also very interested in the people he described as part of his community of care. One was James's best friend, Sean Gallagher.

Sean and James grew up together. They were more like brothers than friends, and I kept wondering what the experience was like for Sean. The impact. I wanted Sean to put a voice to that impact. I wanted to learn more about what he did for his friend, and what he would recommend others do who might find themselves part of a future community of care. I finally got the courage to reach out to Sean, and this young man shared his profound story with me. I told him about this project and asked him if he had any interest in being a part of it. Stunningly, he said yes.

Sean acted as a point of light for his friend during a very dark time. My own 26 points of light, whom you will meet in this book, are some of the people who helped me to get upright, healthy, whole. They literally carried me when I could not carry myself. They illuminated the path in times when I felt such great darkness. You will hear from my husband, my four kids, my extended family, my work associates, my friends, my doctor, and four of the nurses who cared for me for the thirty days that I spent in the hospital receiving chemo.

Those were some incredibly dark days, but I had an amazing community: my tribe of angels who stood with me and helped me find my way back to health. Just as I was impacted by them, each of these points of light were impacted by my diagnosis.

You will hear from each of them about that impact. You will also learn what they were willing to do to impact my getting to the other side of this disease. I have asked each of them to share tangible things that they would recommend others do who are a part of someone else's frontline. You will hear directly from each of them, in their own voices. It is the blending of these voices that I believe makes this collective so incredible.

You should know that every contributor has offered their story for nothing in return. They are not being paid for their work. In fact, proceeds of this book are going to several different cancer research and patient care organizations, including CaringBridge. The intentions of this community of care are to pay it forward, to offer what we learned to others who are getting the diagnosis today. For me, this is a gift back to the world.

As of this writing, I am celebrating five years of remission. I have learned that while everyone's cancer journey is unique, they all have something in common: If you're undergoing the arduous journey I did, you *need* to rely on others. You need to connect and stay connected with your community, whatever that connection means for you.

My hope is that this collection of illuminations and reflections might offer two things:

- If *you* have just received a critical diagnosis, know that *there is hope*. My hope is that this book feels like a blanket of love, encouragement, and comfort, and that these voices can help you better understand those who want to become part of your community of care but don't always know how to help or reach out.

- If you are part of another's community of care, know that *you are not alone.* My hope is that this book will be a resource for you and others in your circle and give you tangible ideas of how to best support the person navigating the diagnosis—wherever you are and whatever your talents.

Know that I understand the impact of the fear, the questions, and the unknown. My mantra was and is *take it a half day at a time.* Sometimes that's the best you've got. Sometimes it feels it is *all* you've got!

One of my sons describes the gift that we as a family have been given as "more." More days, more laughs, more celebrations. I am cognizant of the "more" that I have been given. And truly, this is what I'm offering to you now.

I wish you more . . .

Maureen O'Brien

PART

1

IMMEDIATE FAMILY

AS POINTS OF LIGHT

In the next several chapters, you'll meet my husband, my kids, my siblings, and two of my sisters-in-law. ALL were impacted. You will hear in their own voices about that impact.

The first is my husband, Dan. My sister named him El-mer because he simply was the glue that held the entirety of our family together. Quiet and unassuming, he was the daily strength and reassurance I needed. Often, I would ask him if I was going to die. He would pause, and with conviction, he would say, "There is no evidence that we need to believe that. So no, you are not going to die, and certainly, not today."

Dan kept a calendar of the happenings of every single day during my diagnosis and treatment. (I would highly recom-mend this. Not only because it keeps you on track for all ap-pointments, scans, infusions, and so on, but because later, you will not recall all the things that you went through.) Our lives were consumed with tests, scans, chemo treatments, trips to the cancer center for follow-up shots, calls to the doctor, and runs to the pharmacy. He did all of this while he held down a full-time job.

Dan is my #1 hero. You are also going to meet many other heroes and sheroes in this book. Even five years later, there is not a day that passes that I am not awestruck by the devotion, love, and care that these folks had for me and for my family.

Gathering the chapters for this book has been overwhelming. There was so much I did not remember. I was simply too sick. Now, the abundance of gratitude that I feel for the people who carried me during my journey sustains me to the next scan, or test, or doctor's visit. Often, I'm holding my breath until I hear one more time, "You are cancer-free."

I am aware not everyone will have the same outcome that I did. There are no guarantees for any of us. But there is hope. Always hope. And my hope is that this book will help to sustain you on your own journey, whether you are the patient or part of a community of care.

CHAPTER 1

DAN O'BRIEN

HUSBAND

You already know Dan is my #1 hero! Dan refers to me as "Da Bride" anytime he writes. You will see that others call me MO (short for Maureen and my initials), but for Dan, it's Da Bride. I'm not sure why, except that we live in Chicago, and . . . well, I'm not sure why.

At the date of this publication, God willing, we will have been married for thirty-nine years. Dan is the calmest, kindest person in the world. While I am like a tornado, he is like a soft, spring rain. He's also a pretty funny guy. When people ask him about our marriage of thirty-nine years, he always says, "Feels like five minutes . . . under water!"

*Dan, in his writing, talks about **"awareness of the gifts."** It is something he has taught me. Awareness. In* *his quiet, unassuming way, he has taught me about love through his actions. The lesson has been more than could be taught with words. Dan is pure love in human form. I know that you will hear through Dan's words the conviction of faith, hope, and love. He is a gift to our family. Now, I know he'll be a gift to you.*

I was sitting on a bench in the waiting room. It was January of 2016. The doctor had just told Da Bride that she did not have a torn rotator cuff. He said that she had a soft tumor, the size of a baseball, located in her upper arm. He recommended that we see an oncologist right away.

You hope to never hear those words in a lifetime, no matter how old you get. What is the standard reaction when your stomach drops so far that it disconnects your facial muscles? I looked at Da Bride, attempting no reaction. My face remained the same while hundreds of thoughts ran through my head. Fear, dismay, anger, defiance, and rebellion took me far from the familiar rock of faith. I was flailing in a stormy sea of thoughts. The universe slowed down at that moment. I heard myself say, "Do you have a recommendation? Where would you go if it were your wife?" The doctor replied that there was a cancer center on the other side of town and that he could make a phone call to let them know that we were coming. His answer gave me time to center myself and lightly pick up the reins of family leadership. We thanked him, said good-bye, and drove off into the sunset, literally.

Our lives were about to change.

Leadership in our family is best done from the rear of the pack. You don't have to fight for the position, and it is always available whether you want it or not. The phrase *herding cats* comes to mind whenever I think of leading our family. Everyone has their own idea of what should be done. They simply head off in a direction and assume that the rest of us are following. Living among natural leaders is great, but now it seemed everyone was looking to me for direction. I had been thrust to the front of the pack, a rather unfamiliar position. Da Bride's cancer was going to be the challenge of a lifetime, and her life might depend on our success.

There are three rocks that I carry in life. One of them is the thought that whatever happens is no surprise to God; it is only a surprise to me. I dwell on that thought in the important moments in my life. It helps me find the eye of the storm. In the eye of the storm, there is a calm that allows a way forward with confidence. I do not control my path; I simply follow the eye of the storm. With the other two rocks of humility and obedience, I can live quite peacefully in the greatest whirlwinds of my life. This is where I try to live when I am most afraid, most confused, and most distressed. When I get there, I wonder why I left. Of course, I leave whenever the storm slows down and I think that I can handle it on my own. Whoa! I should just stay there.

WHATEVER HAPPENS IS NO SURPRISE TO GOD; IT IS ONLY A SURPRISE TO ME.

We began the journey of a thousand appointments. I kept a calendar of events. We called our children and our brothers and sisters. We spent more than a few hours talking with relatives in the medical field. It took a while to name the enemy. After a second opinion our enemy had a name: lymphoma. It was stage 4, and it was the kind that grows the fastest. We had little time, there was a race to be run, and we needed to get started.

February of 2016 was filled with doctor appointments and tests. I still had a full-time job in a factory as a scheduler with additional purchasing duties. I told my boss as much as I knew about the situation, which felt like an onion slowly being peeled. We knew it was serious and it was going to be time-consuming. He worked with me to get me set up to work remotely. I resolved to go with Da Bride to all the tests and doctor appointments that I could. My boss was a huge sup-porter of that resolution, and I never missed any of them. It got a little complicated when I needed to juggle conference calls with "being in the room" for doctor's rounds, but my boss covered for me and things worked out superbly. I probably did not thank him enough—what a gift!

My early years had prepared me for this challenge without my awareness. As a ten-year-old child, I had a farm accident and needed to stay in the hospital for a week. The hospital was in a town twenty-five miles from the farm, and I was one of four children. I remember that my mom would come visit ev-ery day for a few hours. Some days, she was able to come twice. Hospitals had visiting hours in those days, and I felt alone much of the time. Mostly the nights. I remember wondering if I was going to die and they just weren't talking about it.

My parents had also prepared me for this challenge. They helped care for my widowed grandmothers and a great-aunt over a period of years. One at a time, they each needed help living in their homes as they got older. My mom and dad traveled to their homes a few times a week. They took them to doctor appointments and fixed things in their homes. They helped with cleaning and laundry. All these great ladies lived well into their nineties. My parents spent time with them so that they would not be alone—what a gift!

As February was ending, a treatment plan was taking shape. A friend of Da Bride, Britta McKenna, whom you will hear from later in this book, volunteered to help organize our lives. She volunteered to bring order to our little family. I was a rookie at being the lead caregiver, and I think she knew it. With our permission, she set up a website at caringbridge.org for communication with family and friends. She was not only talented but experienced—she had learned of this platform in her own fight with cancer. She became our master scheduler. What a gift of time.

Time to be with Da Bride was at a premium. Da Bride's treatment plan included six chemo treatments, three weeks apart. Each treatment was a five-day stay at the local hospital. Remembering my childhood experience, I resolved to be with the Da Bride as much as possible. Before COVID, hospital visiting hours had changed. It was possible to have someone with Da Bride for the entire time. I resolved that as much as possible, Da Bride would not be alone.

We called on family members with some healthcare background and a few close friends, and we arranged to have someone with Da Bride whenever I could not be there. Several people were watching me to make sure that I was getting the proper rest. Permission to sleep is also a gift.

We were able to have someone with Da Bride continuously during her six chemotherapy treatments. We were able to alert the staff when a bag had been drained and a new one needed to be started. We provided conversation in the middle of the night when a patient's mind can wander or needlessly worry. Peace of mind is a great gift in life.

Chemotherapy knocks down the immune system nearly completely. We needed to limit the number of visitors to the minimum needed to take care of Da Bride. Many friends, neighbors, and extended family were excluded. The scheduler took some heat. We felt bad that it was so and asked these people for their prayers. Indeed, we asked almost everyone that we knew for their prayers.

Some people took this request and ran with it. They reported their efforts, and we were gratified to hear that our neighbors and people in many cities and states were holding us up in their prayers and prayer groups. We even heard of people in Ireland, England, Spain, Italy, and other countries praying for us. The spiritual gift of prayer is the most awesome gift. It may not be so, but it seems as if one can physically feel the support when being prayed for by large numbers of people. At any rate, there is power in prayer, and it is probably the greatest gift you can give.

THERE IS POWER IN PRAYER, AND IT IS
PROBABLY THE GREATEST GIFT YOU CAN GIVE.

We were blessed in many ways during this time. So many people wanted to provide a meal for us that a neighbor needed to coordinate the effort. What a gift of time by the coordinator and the meal provider. It allowed us to eat without taking the time to prepare the meal.

Ultimately, we learned about an organization in our area called Fox Valley Food for Health (fvffh.org), an organization that couples high school kids with chefs to prepare nutrient-rich meals for families going through significant health issues. The meals (for the entire family) are delivered at no charge. Imagine . . . not having to think about or shop for meals. Just having them show up on your doorstep by delivery angels. Such a gift.

Some people left their families, children, and grandchildren to help us in our time of need. We thanked them and continue to be grateful for their time, advice, and company. We asked them to convey our thanks to their families for allowing them to come. We are aware that without the support of their families, those caregivers would not have been able to help us when we needed their help. Giving the gift of another's presence is a great gift indeed.

Dr. Robert Bayer of Northwestern Medicine and Dr. Sonali Smith of the University of Chicago directed our care. They provided the first and second opinions on the lymphoma diagnosis. Their cooperation allowed us to get chemotherapy treatments at our local hospital and provided the transition from one hospital system to another for the extended care. Their cooperative management style allowed us to be a part of the decisions in forming and executing the treatment plan for Da Bride. Cooperation between hospitals is not mandated. The collaboration between these two doctors was exceptional and a great gift to us.

Dr. Bayer made some excellent decisions in preparing Da Bride for chemotherapy. He directed a metal rod be placed in her leg to support the thigh bone, which had been weakened by the cancer. Chemotherapy can also weaken the bones so that a simple fall can break a large bone. We did not want the patient to have a broken leg during chemotherapy.

The lymphoma was among the most aggressively growing the doctors had seen. This was driving the need to start the first round of treatment right away. Da Bride had a slight fever. The insertion of the metal rod less than two weeks earlier could have been the source of the fever, but lab tests showed a slight indication of strep or flu virus. If we started chemotherapy and took down her immune system, a simple infection might become a huge problem. Da Bride was getting much weaker, the cancer was growing fast, and there was no conclusive data as to the source of the fever.

Dr. Bayer waited one day. When the fever was unchanged, he ordered chemotherapy to begin the next day. Had he waited another week, the lymphoma might not have been survivable. That would not be an educated opinion, only the opinion of one who grew up on a farm sometimes observing creatures on the edge between life and death. Dr. Bayer gave the gift of action when "waiting for more data" would have given more confidence to the decision at great cost to the patient. We are so grateful.

Dr. Sonali Smith was a breath of fresh air and renewed confidence when we arrived in her care after completing the six chemotherapy treatments. She was a member of a teaching hospital (the University of Chicago) and familiar with the latest research on lymphoma. She was able to prescribe a treatment plan with minimal impact. And she installed a greater level of confidence in a patient who had picked up the reins of her treatment.

Da Bride was now worried at the slightest indication that the cancer was returning. Dr. Smith patiently explained that three indicators needed to be watched for interaction. She told Da Bride that to be concerned about the elevation of just one of the indicators was to worry needlessly. After hearing this repeated many times, Da Bride began to worry less. Dr. Smith patiently gave the gift of confidence. Could there be a better or more important gift to a worried patient?

Along the journey, the mailman continued to deliver cards and letters. Almost everyone sent a card when they heard the news, and we saved them all for quite a while. There was a time, at the beginning, where we had to read them to Da Bride. We are thankful for each card and letter. The time people take to select a card and write a note or letter is also a gift.

What also stands out in our memories is the effect of receiving multiple cards and letters. It has a different effect on the family and the patient than electronic communication. Perhaps it is the more personal touch. I do not know. I only witnessed the positive effect it had on Da Bride and her recovery. Perhaps it was enhanced by the need to keep people away for fear of infection and disease while her immune system was recovering.

Our family also became closer on this journey. Our sisters-in-law joined our little family, and we really got to know and appreciate each other. We learned about their families as they learned about ours. They would drop in and out for a week at a time, sometimes not even crossing paths. Friends would stay the night in the hospital or cover daytime hours when I needed to be at work. All were careful to join the more distant group whenever they felt sick so that Da Bride could stay as healthy as possible. This caution is also a gift, and it often goes unseen or unthanked. Thank you to those who kept a distance so that we could heal.

> THE JOURNEY HAS AWAKENED A SENSE OF GRATITUDE IN ME. PEOPLE IMPRESS ME NOW IN THEIR ACTS OF KINDNESS. I DON'T THINK I WOULD HAVE NOTICED OR ACKNOWLEDGED THEM BEFORE.

This has been a learning experience for me. It rekindled some family ties. It strengthened other family ties. It really has been a journey of increasing gratitude. I am grateful that Da Bride recovered. I am grateful to all who helped in that effort, even if it seemed small to them. Most of all, the journey has awakened a sense of gratitude in me. People impress me now in their acts of kindness. I don't think I would have noticed and certainly not acknowledged them before January of 2016.

A *sticky wicket* comes from the game of cricket. It is a metaphor that refers to a difficult circumstance. I am grateful for the sticky wicket. The sticky wicket of January 2016 attracted kindness from neighbors, friends, family, business associates, and strangers. It reignited lost friendships and repaired a few others. It added a whole new personal level to a few business associates, who became our friends through their compassion. We heard from friends for the first time in years. It brought the world a little closer to us, and we found kindness in abundance. We found that people genuinely cared about us because they told us so in their prayers, words, and actions.

In return, we found increased kindness in our way of living. Wouldn't it be nice to live in a world where we were all a little kinder and gentler with each other? How would that feel? What would that look like in the way we lived our lives? We might understand how to disagree and remain peaceable. We might even be able to live in peace. I wouldn't choose the sticky wicket of January 2016, but it left our family better than it found us. Sometimes the sticky wicket is a gift that you do not realize until you're on the other side of it. I am grateful for the learnings of the sticky wicket of 2016.

WOULDN'T IT BE NICE TO LIVE IN A WORLD WHERE WE WERE ALL A LITTLE KINDER AND GENTLER WITH EACH OTHER?

ILLUMINATIONS

If you've been impacted by a critical diagnosis, these are a few gifts you can offer your loved one (and yourself).

- The gift of sleep. If someone you love is helping a loved one through a challenging diagnosis, make sure they get enough rest.

- The gift of time. Taking care of something time consuming like meal planning offers relief to a family already burning the candle at both ends.

- The gift of caution. Staying away from a patient with a compromised immune system is difficult but often necessary, and that caution is always appreciated.

- The gift of peace of mind. Companionship and conversation—or simply being there in case you're needed—is an incredible gift.

- The gift of communication. Sending a card or letter every so often gives the family and the patient the sense that someone is with them on the journey.

MAUREEN'S STORY

Journal Entry by Dan O'Brien
March 2016

All,

Da Bride has been patronizing several doctors for the past several weeks. Something wasn't quite right in December. Persistent cough and sore shoulder with some fever, especially at night. In January we went to the family doctor to get antibiotics for the cough and an orthopedic surgeon for the shoulder. The cough survived the antibiotics. We thought the shoulder pain was a "torn rotator cuff". The surgeon gave her a cortisone shot and sent her to rehab. Rehab sent her back to the surgeon after a week or so as Mo's condition was not going to get any better in rehab. An MRI was performed and a meeting with the surgeon revealed that it was not a torn rotator cuff—it was a tumor, likely cancerous.

February was spent at Northwestern Medicine Delnor Hospital with more MRIs, mammograms, CAT scans, bone biopsy, bone marrow biopsy, and a PET scan. The diagnosis was "diffuse large B-cell non-Hodgkin's lymphoma," and it was the most aggressive version. Maureen's disease presents itself both in the blood and on the bone, which is unusual. The tumor was eroding the upper bone of her arm. Scans revealed lesions on her leg bone which had weakened it to the point that a surgery was needed to prevent a fracture. A rod was put in her leg on Feb 26 at Delnor Hospital in Geneva, IL, part of the Northwestern Health System. The question was whether a similar operation should be performed on her shoulder. If so, it would need to be done at the University of Chicago.

Early March was spent gathering a second opinion at the University of Chicago. The diagnosis was confirmed, and the orthopedic surgeon recommended that shoulder surgery be delayed so that chemotherapy could begin. The cancer was so aggressive and so much time had been used to diagnose the DNA makeup of the cancer that treatment was more imperative than surgery.

Maureen began treatment March 11. Her chemotherapy requires a hospital admission and runs for five consecutive days, if there are no delays it is repeated every 2-3 weeks depending on how well she rebounds. Da Bride came home from her first chemo late afternoon on St. Patrick's Day, our son Sean's birthday. We are still waiting to see how well she rebounds to schedule the next round of chemo.

While this journey has been difficult, it has reminded us how well blessed we are with family and friends who all care about us and desire to help. There is never enough prayer in the world and to the extent that any of us can make that different . . . that would be a help. It is a true comfort to know that many, many other people are praying for us.

Thank you to everyone who has or will remember us in their prayers before the Lord.

The Dan O'Brien Family
Dan, Maureen, Liam, Charles, Sean, and Elizabeth

PROTOCOL BEGINS

Journal Entry by Britta McKenna
March 11, 2016

This morning Maureen begins her first round of chemo at Delnor. The family is eager to get the protocol underway to stop the spread of cancer and thanks everyone for their support, prayers, food and love. The family also is asking at this time that due to the effects of chemo on Maureen's immune system that we keep the germs to a minimum by not visiting her at the hospital at this time. The type of chemo being used will be infused first through the spinal column to get more immediate effect and she'll be hospitalized during the course of chemo over the next five days.

Please post your words of encouragement to the family on this guestbook or mail her a card. You can also sign up on Maureen's MealTrain page to bring the family a meal.

Thank you for your continued prayers for Maureen and her family.

CHAPTER 2

LIAM O'BRIEN

ELDEST CHILD, SON

*As the oldest, Liam had perhaps the greatest burden to carry. Liam was the only child still living at home at the time of my diagnosis, and he was working for my company. He had the difficult circumstance of watching the day-to-day decline and difficulties of cancer. Here, Liam offers prudent advice on **"things for the journey,"** which includes caring for SELF as a member of the community of care.*

Liam will help you to remember that you must do the things that feed your own soul so that you are able to go the distance on the journey.

I was living with my parents and working in the family business in 2016, the year my mother was diagnosed with stage 4 lymphoma. I remember being angry when I first heard the news. This all started as just some shoulder pain, what we thought might have been a torn rotator cuff. Mom is the toughest person I know, so when she started having pain in her shoulder in December 2015 and then went to the doctor thirty days later, I thought for sure we were headed for a simple shoulder procedure.

I REMEMBER BEING ANGRY WHEN I FIRST HEARD THE NEWS.

We *were* headed for surgery, but it wasn't that simple.

The first step was to get an MRI of the "tear." Mom and Dad went to get an MRI, and by the time they got home, there was a message from the shoulder surgeon on the machine. At the time I thought it was weird, but not weird enough to ask any questions. A couple of hours later, they returned from the doctor's office, and my mom was ghostlike in color.

This next part is a bit of a blur. I remember hearing the word *tumor*, and that they didn't know anything yet. The conversation might have only included those two things—I'm just not sure. I felt like I mentally ran away, just tried to block it all out.

I remember snapping back into the conversation when my parents proposed not telling my other siblings until they had more information. I was expected to be the guardian of this secret until further notice? Vehemently, I objected. I knew that I wouldn't be able to keep that from my brothers. I'm the oldest of four (three boys and a girl), and my brothers and I are extremely close. We were supposed to keep this a secret from people who ultimately would become part of this crucial community of care? To me, this was wrong. No matter what the outcome, my siblings would always blame me for leaving them in the dark. I remember arguing, pleading, and persuading my mom and dad to tell the rest of the kids that night. I set up a video call so that we could all at least see each other. Easily the worst Google Hangouts meeting I ever had to do. The first of many.

We decided in that first meeting that moving forward, we would use the chat feature of Google Hangouts to distribute information as it came in. We liked the idea of the running feed as opposed to a group text message. We also liked the idea of using video whenever possible. While we are a close-knit family emotionally, geographically we were not.

After that first meeting, Mom deteriorated rapidly. She needed surgeries for a biopsy, a port for chemo, and a rod in her leg. Miraculously, her doctor was able to call in every favor he had and scheduled all three procedures as one surgery (three surgeons, two different ORs). My dad and I waited in the hospital lobby almost the entire day, and I gave a running commentary in Google Hangouts about the incoming updates. The surgery was successful, and we were asked to follow the doctor to a small office for a post-op explanation.

The news was mixed. The procedures were successful; however, the damage to her shoulder and her hip/thigh was more extensive than anticipated. I think the doctor was trying to do us a kindness by choosing his words carefully, but he clearly knew it was bad. All I cared about was seeing my mom. Finally, the doctor gave us the room number, and Dad and I hurried off to see her.

If you have ever watched someone come out of general anesthesia, you know that it's a harrowing experience. In my head, I had expected that Hallmark movie "wake from a long nap" moment with my mom fully cognitive. What happened was the rigors. She was convulsing and talking to people who were not there.

I panicked. I gave a weak excuse to my dad about going home to care for, feed, and let out the family dog. Really, I was terrified, and I did not want either my mom or dad to see it. They would immediately change their focus and try to console me. But that day, it wasn't about me. I posted in Google Hangouts that she had made it through surgery and that things seemed stable. I wanted my siblings to know, and I was trying to protect my dad from continuous calls and texts. I felt like he really needed to just be with his wife and not worry about the rest of us.

My brother, Sean, and I moved a twin bed from the upstairs guest room to our family room on the first floor. From our conversation with the surgeon, we knew that Mom would not be able to navigate stairs. I also knew that her long road to recovery would not be comfortable on the couch.

The next two weeks were a whirlwind. We got the diagnosis: stage 4 diffuse large B-cell non-Hodgkin's lymphoma. At first, I honestly was relieved. At least we knew what we were fighting. Unfortunately, I remember that relief did not last, and simply knowing what it was did not give us the lift we were hoping for.

Cancer sucks.

Soon after the diagnosis, my mom's sisters and brother flew in to visit. As my uncle Bill was leaving, he pulled me aside. He shook my hand, looked me dead in the eyes, and said, "Take care of my sister." As an older brother myself, the gravity of the situation really cemented itself into my core. I needed to do whatever was necessary to help relieve the pressure for Dad so that he could help hold my mom up. She needed every ounce of her toughness to fight the disease and get well again.

We hit rock bottom that Friday, almost two weeks to the day after the surgery. Mom had a fever and had to be rushed to the emergency room. She was not completely coherent, but she was complaining about having the chills. I remember that in the ER, the decision was made to have her admitted. The oncologist wanted to have her brought to the oncology floor, but it wasn't possible while she had a fever. A virologist was brought in to monitor for infections, and Mom was moved to a room in the hospital to be monitored overnight. My little sister, Lizzy, came up from Bloomington, Illinois, electing to stay with Mom overnight. Lizzy shared later that it was an incredibly hard night. Attempting to break the fever, the nurses had taken all the blankets and were icing my mom. Mom was freezing and crying out desperately for help. There was nothing Lizzy could do but watch and try to comfort her.

Cancer sucks.

Saturday morning brought two room changes. The fever was down. Mom was lucid. However, she had developed a cough, and there were growing concerns about pneumonia. Chest scans and X-rays were ordered. There were still symptoms of fluid in her chest. More scans, more tests, more doctors. A good friend of mine, Mike Garrity, called and asked me to go fishing. I needed a break. I agreed. This was (is) a marathon. I'd encourage anyone going through this to take breaks where you can.

Kathy Garrity, Mike's mom and a very good friend of my mom, knew what was happening. Mike understood. At the same time, his mom was going through treatment for ovarian cancer. Years earlier, she had beaten breast cancer. I was absolutely sure he understood what I was feeling. Sometimes, conversations with other friends moved into pity, or at least what felt to me like pity. I'm certain it was well-intentioned, but it was not what I wanted or needed. With Garrity, I could just talk about fishing, or how cancer sucks. It's not like Mike was a wealth of wisdom. In fact, it was unusual if anything was met with more than a "yep." But somehow, it was enough.

When I got home that evening, a neighbor had brought food. I learned that Britta McKenna was coming to help us get organized. My mom was always the organizer. Now, that role was vacant, and we felt it.

Britta was (is) a godsend. She helped us the most by offering to be the gatekeeper. Anyone outside of our family that wanted to see Mom had to go through Britta. Mom has a large network of friends in our area, and people wanted to offer sympathy and well wishes. They wanted to see her for themselves.

In the weeks that followed, it was nice to have a person outside the family who could field the calls, questions, and concerns about Mom. Britta also offered to manage the "how can I help" line. It was a relief to hand off to Britta when people would ask what they could do. It felt good to say, "Oh my gosh, thank you. I'm not sure. But ask Britta. I know she is keeping a list of things. I really appreciate that you're asking."

Another critical piece that Britta took on was to help start and maintain the CaringBridge site, where the latest information on my mom could be disseminated. She did this until my mom was strong enough to write herself. CaringBridge gives a family the gift of a free platform to share information so that it's not necessary to recount the entire story every time you bump into someone you know (or, more accurately, knows your mom).

When Sunday morning came, my dad and I went to church. I was raised Catholic, and I guess you could say my parents are relatively devout. I try to at least attend Mass with my parents when I visit. After Mass, we went straight to the hospital. I remember joking that we could stop and get a better breakfast before heading to the hospital, but Dad was very concerned we would miss the doctor's rounds. When we entered the hospital, I offered to go get some breakfast items from the cafeteria. I headed off to buy an energy drink for me, a coffee for Dad, and some muffins to share.

When I arrived at Mom's room, doctors were huddled and congregated around her hospital bed. I walked into the room and handed Dad his coffee. The doctors reintroduced themselves for my benefit. There was a neurologist, a virologist, her GP, and her oncologist. I had unknowingly interrupted a very lively discussion about the best course of action going forward. The virologist and neurologist seemed to think that starting Mom's treatment was dangerous. Apparently, neurology had been called in to evaluate her because one of her scans seemed to show signs that she had recently had or was having a stroke.

Virology was concerned that her symptoms were not part of the cancer but a separate infection. Wiping out her immune system was detrimental to her ability to recover from basic illnesses, and the common cold might kill her. Dr. Bayer, her oncologist at the time, was advocating that the treatment should begin immediately. He believed that the symptoms were all related to her body trying to fight off the cancer and that any further delays would increase an already astronomically high chance of death.

I remember after Dr. Bayer stopped speaking, the room was silent. My dad stood there without movement or sound for what seemed like an eternity, just trying to process everything he had just been told. Then, my dad, in the most assertive tone I'd ever heard him use in my life, simply declared, "Start the treatment."

⬡　　⬡　　⬡

At this point, it would be good to note that I hate hospitals. I hate being in them. I hate the way they smell. Mom's chemo treatment was a five-day continuous drip of drugs. Most I had never heard of, but it looked like she was getting a primo mix of red, orange, and green Hi-C. That's how you know things are bad: the IV glows in the dark. Or it's so bright you can still see it when you close your eyes.

My aunt Jan came from Minnesota for a couple of weeks at a time to help take care of my mom. She would help her bathe, go to the bathroom, get dressed. She helped her do all the "little things" that we take for granted until we are rendered incapable of doing them. Aunt Jan would sleep on the couch next to my mom, just in case she needed anything. She constantly shooed my dad away so that he would get some rest. As I recall this experience, I realize how lucky we were (are) to have such clear demonstrations of love and advocacy for our family.

The treatment protocol was one week of treatment and then two weeks off. During the treatment week, I would come by from work at lunchtime. I would stop at the cafeteria and buy a piece of carrot cake. Carrot cake was a favorite of my grandpa, my mom's father, who had passed away a few years prior. My mom loved it too. Somehow, I thought that if she and I shared the carrot cake, we might be able to channel my grandpa's energy or presence somehow. He was a courageous and tough man, and he was deeply caring. I knew we needed his fire to get through the treatment protocol. It's funny what you do and what you believe when you're in this circumstance. I was willing to call on anyone to help my mom get well.

I tried to limit my time with my mom while she was in treatment. One, because I hate hospitals, and I didn't want my anxiety to become her anxiety, but the second reason is that twenty minutes was an eternity for her. You could really tell that the treatment was mentally and physically taxing. While my mom never said anything about it, I could tell that after about a twenty-minute visit, she was done. She needed to rest and just focus on healing. On my way home, I would often find myself talking to God. Less outright conversation, and more just begging for one more lunch with my mom.

After the second round of treatment, my girlfriend at the time called with some news that made me furious. At the time, I was living in my parents' basement. Following the call, I came upstairs, and I'm sure the fury showed on my face. My mom's frail voice called out to me, so I went over to the foot of her bed in the family room.

"What's wrong?" she asked meekly.

"Nothing, Mom," I said, doing my best to compartmentalize.

"Are you mad?" she asked, prodding me.

"No, Mom. I'm fine. I just have to go out for a minute," I said.

"Are you mad at me? Because I'm sick?" she asked.

I was absolutely gutted. Fighting back tears, I managed to squeak out that I wasn't mad at her, something else had come up. I remember walking away under her skeptical stare. I felt horrible. I had let something so stupid and trivial jeopardize me, which ultimately influenced my mom. She shouldn't have to be worrying about me or my feelings. She should only be focusing on getting well.

A couple weeks later, Mom started to round the corner. So many days I wondered if she would ever fully come back to us. She was frail and weak, and often there was no light in her eyes. After her third or fourth round of chemo, something wonderful happened. My mom looked up at my aunt Jan, who was sitting on the end of her bed, and said, "This carpet is filthy."

My aunt Jan jumped up and exclaimed, "*She's back!* She's coming back to us!"

Following that, my mom really started to get stronger. She was able to do more. She could sit with us at the dinner table and hold a conversation. She still would get fatigued, but we could tell that she believed she was going to make it through this. It was a lift we all desperately needed.

Her last treatment week began on July 4, 2016. We believed the date was not coincidental. We were in the home stretch. Mom would be "independent," free from cancer at the end of the week.

The fabulous nurses at Northwestern Hospital must have believed the same. They had decorated my mom's room with balloons and congratulatory banners so that when she entered on that first day of her last round, she would realize she was close to the finish line. All the nurses and attendants who had cared for my mom were in her room. They cheered. They laughed, and they cried. We celebrated the end of this hellish marathon that Mom had run.

Five very long days later, I went to my mom's room to help my dad bring her home for the final time. We thanked the nurses, doctors, and hospital staff for taking such great care of our family, and we quietly joked that we hoped to never see them again. We are still in awe of the inspired work, love, care, and long hours the nurses and staff put in. They certainly were part of our community of care, and we are forever grateful.

ILLUMINATIONS

As I sit here, almost five years later, thinking about how we managed to survive that tempestuous period of our lives, I am struck by three things that really helped position us for success:

1. It's essential to have a gatekeeper and a centralized place for disseminating information (like CaringBridge). That was critical. It allowed us to focus on tasks at hand (like listening fully to the doctor during rounds).

2. It's OK to go fishing (or however you relax). Because this is a marathon, there are going to be days where you literally can't take one more thing. Remember that the caregiver needs a break too. Go and fish (or do whatever you do to recharge your batteries), and come back ready for what's next. The patient is going to need your positivity to keep going.

3. Focus only on the things you can control. That's going to be a challenge because everything is going to be in flux. That's OK. Try to use the flow to get to where you need to be. If you use all your energy fighting the current, there won't be anything for you to give the patient you are trying to care for.

ROUND 1, DAY 2

Journal Entry by Britta McKenna
March 12, 2016

Maureen tolerated her spinal infused chemotherapy yesterday and had an IV round today. She was in good spirits and was able to sit in the chair most of the day. Family is all home and giving her strength as are your cards and prayers. An angel nurse stopped by today with a wonderful personal story of her miraculous recovery from a grave illness. The good fight is well underway! The family thanks everyone for the outpouring of love and tasty meals. Pink tulips and a beautiful vase from Mariann and Sharon brighten Mo's room and remind us that spring is just around the corner.

ROUND 1, DAY 3

Journal Entry by Britta McKenna

March 13, 2016

Maureen received IV chemo today and remains in good spirits, though a bit worn out from all the activity on Saturday. Dan "went shopping" for her this afternoon and brought back some ice eye packs and a few surprises. Mo's bag of fun included St. Paddy's Day window stickers, green bow ties, a leprechaun bracelet and an Irish princess blinking green bejeweled tiara. In classic Mo style, she offered the tiara to her favorite nurse, who was "crowned" and proceeded on her rounds with a bounce in her step. A few more days in the hospital, then headed home, hopefully on St. Patrick's Day!

CHAPTER 3

CJ O'BRIEN

SECOND CHILD, SON

> *CJ was living out of state when I was first diagnosed. Imagine the incredible difficulty of knowing that your mom, someone you believed could not be taken down, was in serious health trouble. He made the decision to move back to Chicago to help, to hold, to heal.*
>
> *CJ writes about the importance of **"showing up,"** which was precisely what he did and still does. Show up. All of us can show up in some way. We can do whatever is possible for us. And that makes all the difference.*

My mom is my biggest fan. I participated in a lot of activities growing up, and I can't remember a single event, show, or game when she wasn't there. She must have sat through hundreds of hours of football games, track meets, band concerts, plays, graduations, spelling bees, children's choir shows, Frisbee tournaments, and many other soccer/baseball/YMCA basketball games. What's more, I was one of her four active kids, so she had more than just my schedule to manage! To this day I don't know how she was able to make it to all our events on top of her own work and life commitments.

Better known as Maureen O'Brien, my mom is a power woman—an entrepreneur, owner of multiple businesses, and a motivational speaker—and she's loud. Like, really loud. As a former cheerleader and the youngest in a family of six, I suppose she had to be loud in order to be heard!

I can hear her voice now as I recall these memories and am still ducking my head pretending that I don't know her. But regardless of my adolescent feelings of embarrassment, trying to play it cool in front of my friends and coaches, I knew she was supporting me in the best way she knew how while having fun by immersing herself in the activities I was doing. She was still a cheerleader at heart, and my biggest fan.

I grew up in Illinois, but after college I moved around a lot—from Miami to Madison to Denver to Cincinnati—as I worked my way up the corporate ladder. I remember calling home one night in late 2015 and mom mentioned her shoulder was bothering her. It sounded like just a nuisance of pain, and she was having trouble carrying her suitcase through the airport during her recent work travels. It seemed like maybe she had a torn rotator cuff or just a sore shoulder, but she couldn't remember doing anything specific that would've injured it. She said it felt like she had slept on it funny, but it was still nagging for some reason. I didn't think much of it at the time. Parents get old, their bones get tired. We hung up the phone and I figured she'd be back to normal when I called to check in again after a few weeks.

I only have a blurred memory of the crazy series of events that followed. There was a doctor's appointment to check out her shoulder. An X-ray that looked concerning. A sudden hospital admission. An aggressive treatment to fight an aggressive cancer. What cancer? Next came a surgery to stabilize her femur. Weren't we talking about a rotator cuff?

I THINK SOMETIMES WE GET SO CAUGHT UP IN OUR OWN LIVES WE AREN'T PREPARED TO HEAR NEWS LIKE THIS. IT DOESN'T REALLY REGISTER COMPLETELY.

As these events unraveled in February 2016, she was diagnosed with stage 4 non-Hodgkin's lymphoma. I now know this to be a blood cancer, but I had no idea what it was then, and I certainly wasn't ready for what was coming in the months ahead. I think sometimes we get so caught up in our own lives we aren't prepared to hear news like this. It doesn't really register completely; you just keep doing what you're doing. For me, I tend to get way too wrapped up in what I'm working on, and I don't always recognize the gravity beyond the inconvenience that's distracting me from work. At the time I was receiving some of the initial information, I was living in Cincinnati and moonlighting in my first season on the city's (now defunct) American Ultimate Disc League team, I was traveling to Virginia each week for my day job in management consulting, and I was flying to Denver during off weekends to visit my girlfriend of four years.

Mom began treatment in mid-March, but reality didn't sink in for me until late April. The Cincinnati Revolution were scheduled for a game against the Chicago Wildfire on April 23, and I was going to play in front of my home crowd for the first time since I made the pro circuit. I prepared for the game like any other but couldn't help feeling a little more excited that week. I remember running out onto the field under the lights and feeling the surge of adrenaline that comes with playing in front of the people you know. But even before the game began, I knew something was off. There was *something* missing. I remember being up at halftime and searching the crowd, seeing my brothers and my friends in the stands. I couldn't really put my finger on why I wasn't getting the same energy I thought I would get playing in Chicago again.

It finally hit me in the second half that despite the rest of the voices in the stadium, I couldn't hear my mom's rising above everyone else's like I had heard so many times before. The stadium was probably as loud as any other, but it felt eerily quiet. It didn't matter how many people in the crowd were cheering. The atmosphere felt flat, almost numb. My mom wasn't in the stands cheering for me, and the silence was deafening. It was the empty, lonely feeling of a silent sideline.

That was the moment. That's when it really hit that my mom was human. Her cancer diagnosis was more than just some time in the hospital or an evaluation on her health; the strong woman who had started and run three successful businesses, who had published two books, who had raised four O'Brien children, who had spoken fearlessly on stages in front of thousands of people, who was known in our community and active in our schools and city council, the woman I was now taller and stronger than but was somehow still afraid of, was . . . not invincible. Cancer was taking her down.

I can't fully express the crushing realization I felt about seeing her in the hospital. Watching her wince with every movement, looking tired and frail in bed, and seeing her hooked up to monitors and IVs was like experiencing an alternate life that couldn't possibly exist in *our* reality. Mom was weak—that was inconceivable. Mom? Weak? I couldn't think of two words that could be more polar opposite. What are you doing in a hospital bed? Get up and let's get out of here!

I had never been close to anyone who had cancer, so I didn't really know what I could do to support her. I remember wondering, what would you even say when a friend tells you they have cancer? I'm sure I used to say things like "Oh man, I'm so sorry to hear that," or "I'll pray for you," or "Let me know if there is anything that I can do." Now I realized how dull those words sound and how hollow they can feel to a cancer patient or anyone in their community of care. They're certainly well intended and may provide temporary solace, but in the months and weeks of Mom's treatment, there were so many people who wanted to do more and *did* more. That left a lasting impression that I will never forget.

Since I was living in another state and traveling frequently, I tried to put other things on pause and fly home more often, giving my dad relief for a night when I could by staying with Mom at the hospital. I could see how tired and worn he was, but he was like a dog that wouldn't leave his companion's side, and it took effort to get him to relent. He would insist on returning the next day before 7:00 a.m. so he wouldn't miss the moment whenever the doctors checked in, but at least I could convince him to go home and rest. And since he was the constant that kept Mom going, I like to think those returns were doubled.

The heroes and sheroes came out of the woodwork from all corners of our life. There were people I hadn't heard from in years and never expected to show up who did, and it meant the world to our family. Britta McKenna checked in almost every day, set up a CaringBridge page to keep people updated, coordinated dinners and a gardening day to help support not only my mom but also the rest of our family while we dropped everything at home to be there for her, and sometimes even stayed the night in the hospital with Mom during her treatments.

> THE HEROES AND SHEROES CAME OUT OF THE WOODWORK FROM ALL CORNERS OF OUR LIFE. THERE WERE PEOPLE I HADN'T HEARD FROM IN YEARS AND NEVER EXPECTED TO SHOW UP WHO DID, AND IT MEANT THE WORLD TO OUR FAMILY.

Elizabeth Green used her talents as a masseuse and gave Mom daily massages when she was out of the hospital to improve her blood flow and soothe her aching body from the chemo. My mom's sisters, Karen and Patricia, visited from other states whenever they could and checked in with my dad and our medical team whenever they couldn't. My mom's normally stoic brother, Bill, visited from Pittsburgh and helped support us financially. My aunt Jan was a retired nurse and would come down for five or six days at a time from Minnesota to stay with my mom in the hospital and help around the house. Her husband Ron would get up early to make the six-hour drive down and drop her off and check in, then turn around and drive back to work on the farm!

Mary Ann Schira made meals and kept our spirits up. Our neighbors, the Balls, seemed to know exactly when we'd run out of bread and milk and would drop some off whenever they got groceries. The doctors and nurses—Alison, Katie, Dr. Sonali Smith, and too many others to name—provided treatment and care with compassion well beyond their call of duty. And especially my dad—they called him Elmer, like the glue that held us together—who must have gone several weeks on only a few hours of sleep, would work during the day, stay overnight with mom at the hospital, hear the updates from the doctors and repeat them to everyone that asked, manage the bills, and occasionally have time to eat.

There were many more people and acts of love, too many to possibly name them all. But you know what's amazing about all these examples? It's not that everyone made herculean efforts or extraordinary acts of generosity (though some of them certainly did); it's that they all made thoughtful, manageable contributions using the time and talents they had. They all gave generously what they could to support my mom and our whole family.

ILLUMINATIONS

The support we received was overwhelming at times. It still fills my heart to this day when I look back and think about how much people really cared. They didn't just send cards or text messages or prayers— *they showed up.* They didn't ask what they could do to help; they just did it. Anyone walking with someone through a crisis can do the same thing. Mow their lawn, shovel their driveway, send a note and don't ask or expect a response, visit them at the hospital or at home, send an ice facemask or foot coolers, watch their dog, send a gift card, bring in their mail, vacuum their house, take out their trash.

Gary Chapman's *The Five Love Languages* is my favorite book to reference when thinking about ways you can show someone you love them; use the strengths you're most comfortable with, whether it's acts of service, words of affirmation, quality time, giving gifts, or physically showing up and holding their hand. Even if you feel like you can't be the loud cheerleader for the patient, be on the sideline for the caretaker. Supporting the supporter is often what's needed the most but tended to the least. No matter how you choose to show love, I find that the real key here is that a small, truly selfless act will go much further than grand gestures with an expectation of acknowledgment or thanks.

Mother Teresa once said, "Your true character is most accurately measured by how you treat those who can do nothing for you." If you're a primary caretaker for a cancer patient, your strength and positivity will keep them going as much as their own does. If you have the time and capacity to support the primary caretaker for a cancer patient, to be the invisible ally that keeps them going so they can keep the patient going, that will mean the world to them. And, if you don't have the time but you *make* the time, it will mean even more. Giving out of your excess isn't really any charity, but giving until it hurts—until it affects your ability to do or buy the things you would have done otherwise—is the truest meaning of generosity. In my experience, we all have the same twenty-four hours in a day; it's up to you to decide how you spend it.

My life changed through my mom's battle with cancer. I have a better understanding of the way the community helps a person beat a disease. I've learned to slow down and not focus on work all the time, and most importantly, I've learned to appreciate the people who show up for me. I took for granted all the times my mom was in the crowd cheering for me. You don't realize what you have until it's gone, and that memory of the eerily quiet stadium and my silent sideline reminds me not to take my family and my supporters for granted.

If you are going through a similar journey and you want to make an impact, but you aren't sure how, my advice to you is simple: *show up*. Whether you're the loud cheerleader for the patient directly or you're the silent support for the supporter, showing up in these dark times will be the most powerful way to show you care. When you know someone has a tough game ahead, as they're preparing, you can wish them good luck, or you can be there at the game. When you have this opportunity, which will you choose?

PREPARING FOR MY FIRST CHILD

Personal Journal Entry by CJ O'Brien

December 27, 2019

I'm only now beginning to really appreciate all of this as I await the coming of my first child and I think about how my life will change when he arrives. I think about life in my twenties and going to happy hours, playing in softball leagues, traveling for work and for fun, visiting friends out of state, partying on weekends, and generally doing whatever I want to do. I think about how all of this is going to change, and how soon I'll be attending soccer games and piano recitals and school concerts, or whatever my son decides he's into. I tend to be very wrapped up in my own work and my own schedule, and I wonder if it will be challenging for me to make all my son's events like my mom made mine.

At the end of the day, I realize that it's a constant choice and sacrifice to be present for people you care about. I'm grateful that my mom taught me this lesson and did it not with words but through her own actions.

ROUGH PATCH, ROUND 1—DAY 4

Journal Entry by Britta McKenna

March 15, 2016

Mo had a tough go last night and a challenging day as the chemo load intensifies in her body incrementally each day. She is battling nausea and is easily tired. No laps around the hospital floor today as she is resting up. We ask no visitors right now to allow her space.

5 ROUND 1 CHEMO COMPLETE!

Journal Entry by Britta McKenna

March 16, 2016

At 8:37 this evening the last drop of chemo was dispensed signaling the end of Round 1! Maureen will be in the hospital for another day minimum and hopes to be home before St. Paddy heads to bed tomorrow. But the doc will make that call and no amount of shamrock shaking will change his mind. The new day will tell.

Good friend Kathy Garrity is directly upstairs from Mo getting rehydrated from her own battle. Prayers for healing to both Mo and Kathy. A reminder that we don't walk alone.

CHAPTER 4

SEAN O'BRIEN

THIRD CHILD, SON

> *Sean and I had been through a tumultuous time in our relationship prior to my diagnosis. All of that was forgotten when I was diagnosed. I guess that's one of the gifts of cancer. It smacks you into realizing that most of the stuff we get worked up about doesn't matter. That when someone we love is in crisis, everything else is forgotten. Regardless of our own feelings, we need to "stay positive" for the patient.*
>
> *Sean did that for me. He made me laugh. He helped me to remember that I was and am more than a cancer diagnosis. He helped me to remember what is important . . . and he helped me to celebrate the mores.*

I agreed to participate in this book because I didn't know what to do or how to feel when my mom was first diagnosed with cancer. I suspect if you're reading this, you might feel the same.

It is my hope that this might help someone else. There is no manual for cancer. Our family was very fortunate to receive an incredible amount of medical, physical, and emotional support.

Having said that, I will never be able to fully express my incredible gratitude to everyone who helped and supported our family during my mom's battle. The impact is/was immeasurable. We could not have done it without you. From the bottom of my heart, thank you.

Before I share my experience, I'll tell you what I learned. If you're reading this right now because someone you love has been diagnosed with cancer, you don't need my story. You need answers and you need a plan. The journey ahead will be incredibly difficult. Being told that someone that you know or love has been diagnosed with cancer can take the air from your lungs and numb your mind. It can be difficult to know what to do next. There will be times you may wonder if you or your loved one are strong enough and if the cancer can be beaten. I want you to know—and *you must believe*—that you are strong enough. *They* are strong enough. It *can* be beaten.

> IF YOU'RE READING THIS RIGHT NOW BECAUSE SOMEONE YOU LOVE HAS BEEN DIAGNOSED WITH CANCER, YOU DON'T NEED MY STORY. YOU NEED ANSWERS AND YOU NEED A PLAN.

There is one area where we hit an unbelievable stroke of luck: we were fortunate enough to have family members in the medical field. My aunt Jan O'Brien had worked as a triage nurse at the

Mayo Clinic, and my aunt Patricia Burkhart was Assistant Dean of Nursing at the University of Kentucky. I know that most people do not have that advantage. We grew up in the northwest suburbs of Chicago. My parents still live there. The hospitals, testing, and doctors they had available were from Northwestern and the University of Chicago. We were incredibly lucky.

Cancer sucks.

I don't remember everything. There are gaps in my memory that may be a result of time passed and/or overall shock, or maybe grace. At first, it was difficult to believe and understand. Then it became overwhelming both in information and emotion.

On February 25, 2016, I found out my mom had been diagnosed with stage 4 diffuse large B-cell lymphoma. My oldest brother, Liam, sent a text to tell me that we needed to have an urgent family meeting. Since we were all no longer under one roof, and Lizzy and CJ were no longer in the same geographical area, we planned to have a video call that evening at 7:00 p.m. This seemed odd to me. We had never had a family meeting through video chat before. We had always discussed important family information when we were all together or called each other with updates. What was the sudden urgency to have a call that night? Without understanding, I decided I'd find out soon enough, and I carried on with my day.

I don't recall much from that video chat. What I do remember is that when I got on the call for the family meeting, I could see my three siblings, my dad, and a ghostlike version of my mom. All the color had been drained from her face.

She gazed off in the distance, and it was almost as though she wasn't there. This incredibly strong woman, my mom, looked frail and scared. My dad sat next to her and struggled to keep his composure while delivering the news of her diagnosis. After visits to the doctor and specialists, the shoulder pain and weakness my mother had been experiencing had been found to be stage 4 diffuse large B-cell non-Hodgkin's lymphoma. It had spread throughout her body, and another "hot spot" had started to deteriorate the bones in her leg and hip.

If you're like me, when you hear this news, you immediately think, "Cancer sucks." Then, if you're like me, you immediately go to the internet. After googling for a while, you learn there are five stages of cancer. However, for the first time in the history of math, zero has value, and that means it only goes to stage 4.

Here is a layman's version of the stages:

- Stage 0—We found cancer. We caught it early, and it appears to still be only where we found it.

- Stage 1—We found cancer. Still early. Still localized. Don't think it got very far.

- Stage 2—We found cancer. We believe it may have moved here and here.

- Stage 3—More advanced than stage 2. We believe it may have moved here, here, and here.

- Stage 4—The cancer has metastasized. The cancer has spread to other parts of the body.

My mom has stage 4 cancer. More specifically, non-Hodgkin's lymphoma. Oh. My. God.

Soon after her diagnosis, she had surgery to repair her leg where the lymphoma had started to eat away at the bone. Going into surgery, she was exhausted and in rough shape, but the surgery had to happen and quickly. When she came out of surgery, we were able to visit her in post-op. She was hardly conscious (in and out, likely due to the anesthesia still wearing off) and had wires/tubes/machines hooked up everywhere.

This first part of the battle was the scariest part for me personally. It shook me to the effect that although small children were not allowed in the room, we brought my daughter Amy, who was three at the time, just in case it was the last time my mom saw her. Amy is the one and only granddaughter. This was the first and last time I allowed anything less than positive thoughts in my head.

When she was released from the hospital, she was no longer able to use the stairs. We had set up a temporary bedroom on the first floor. Someone would be with her at all times in case she needed anything. It was a complete change for her. This strong and *very* independent woman now depended on someone else to do almost everything for her. At first, every single day and every single task was a struggle. It was exhausting to just be up and a part of the conversation, but she kept on fighting. *We* kept on fighting. And she kept getting stronger.

Those around us helped to take the thinking out of everyday tasks and allowed us to focus on being there to help or spend time with my mom. They filled the need before we understood a need was there. The support was incredible. Meals were brought to the house daily by family friends looking for a way to help. They wanted to find out how she was doing and if/when they might possibly get a chance to see her. That outpouring of love and support . . . it's something that, although it may be obvious to others, I never realized or understood until my mom got sick.

The meals that were made for our family were incredibly helpful during her treatment days. I would try to visit with Mom at the hospital for a few hours after work. The schedule was set up so that there was always someone with her. We each committed not to leave the room until the next person arrived so that she would never be alone. There would be days that we might not get home until late at night, only to realize that we had forgotten to eat lunch and/or dinner. Having a meal already prepared kept us from grabbing something quick and unhealthy on the way home or having to make something for ourselves late at night. (Thinking back, this may have also been the most consecutive number of days I have ever eaten vegetables.) Those meals kept us healthy and upright so that we could help her to get healthy and upright.

One afternoon, I remember being alone in my parents' home while my mom was at the hospital receiving treatment. The doorbell rang, and when I opened it, I saw a friend of my mom's. She was holding a meal, and when she saw me, she began to cry uncontrollably. She could not believe this was happening to *my mom*.

NO MATTER WHAT, STAY POSITIVE.

I didn't know what to do. I did the best I could to comfort her and assure her that my mom was going to be OK. She was getting stronger. She *would* be back. I think I said this as much to assure her as to assure myself. No matter what, stay positive. For her, for you, for them.

On July 18 (my dad's birthday), my mom had her final PET scan. July 20, my dad (and we) got the best birthday gift *ever*! My mom was in remission. Every three months for the next couple of years, she would be tested to ensure that she was still cancer-free. We celebrated five years this year on July 20, 2021. I'm not sure COVID will allow the kind of celebration we intended, but *we will celebrate* nonetheless.

We will celebrate the MORES:

- More birthdays
- More anniversaries
- More births
- More New Years
- More Valentines Days
- More St. Patrick's Days (which is also my birthday!)
- More Easters
- More Fourth of Julys
- More Memorial Days
- More boating days!
- More Labor Days
- More Halloweens
- More Christmases
- More laughter, tears, joys, sorrows . . . *life!*

I hope the same for you. I hope you will always celebrate your MORES.

ILLUMINATIONS

The two biggest pieces of advice that I can give to anyone facing this upcoming battle for a family member (or friend) are to **Stay Positive** and to **Be Present.**

1. **Stay positive.** I know. I hear it: "Great advice, Sean: 'have a can-do attitude.' That's #1?" Well, this should be a *great* read. It seems obvious, and at times, it might even seem impossible, but here it is: *fight like hell to stay positive.* There is incredible power behind positive thinking and maintaining a positive attitude. I believe that positivity can impact the body, the mind, and the spirit. I've seen it. I saw it in the faces of my family, our friends, and the hospital staff. Most importantly, I could see the impact it had on my mom. Conversely, I also believe that negativity and doubt can be just as destructive as the cancer itself. If you are a friend or family member of someone battling cancer, stay positive. Never, for any reason, express doubt, negativity, or the slightest indication that the treatment might not work. Believe that it will. Believe that they can and will get better.

2. **Be present.** During the year of this writing, my parents will have been married for thir-

ty-nine years. My dad was with my mom every step of the way during her battle with cancer. He never missed an appointment, visit, or treatment. However, this kind of presence isn't realistic for everyone, and if you're not in the immediate family, it might not be appropriate. Being present doesn't mean you have to go to every hospital visit, treatment, or doctor appointment. We can't all fit in that little room at once anyway! Being present might mean sending a card or flowers, preparing a meal, calling to let them know you're thinking of them, sending regular texts, letting their dog out, or simply offering them time to not think about cancer for a little while.

You have no idea how much of an impact that you make, no matter how big or small you believe your contribution. Even the small things matter! Our family was incredibly lucky to have such great support among those who were willing and able to be present.

Pro tip: If you feel like you need/want to do something more to help, asking, "What can I do to help you?" may not be the best approach. They might not have an immediate answer, or they might be too afraid/proud to ask for help. Instead, get specific: try asking, "Would it be helpful if I ____?"

BACK HOME

Journal Entry by Britta McKenna

March 18, 2016

Maureen checked out of Northwestern the afternoon of St. Paddy's Day and is resting and gaining strength at home. Her two-week at home routine now begins and then she'll be back to the hospital for Round 2 protocol. Lizzy comes home for Easter break Friday to be a great at home hands and heart for her mom. It is nice to see her resting at home surrounded by family quilts and all the stuff that makes her Mo. Blessings to our wonderful network of angels working together to support Mo and the family and to beat this cancer.

CHAPTER 5

ELIZABETH "LIZZY" O'BRIEN

FOURTH CHILD, ONLY DAUGHTER

*After having our three boys, I remember thanking God that our family was complete. God had a different plan. Her name: Lizzy. She is such a bright light. Beautiful. Courageous. God-centered. As the only girl, Lizzy probably saw more than her share of the awful physical trauma caused by cancer. Yet she never wavered. She had to witness things you hope a kid never has to see. Yet her **"trust in God,"** as she will share with you here, enabled her to stay with me and stand with me for every step of the journey. If you allow it, she will be your bright light too.*

When I learned of my mom's diagnosis, I was in my first year of teaching. In case you're not a teacher or don't have any teachers in your family or friend group, let me give you a little insight: the first year of teaching is sort of like looking both ways before crossing the street and then getting hit by an airplane. I mean that in the kindest way possible. I love my job. It's incredibly rewarding, and it's always an adventure, but man, that first year is *tough*. So now imagine you're on that street, you just got hit by the airplane, you start to stand up, and then a submarine falls on you. Simply doesn't make sense, right? That pretty much sums up the first year of teaching with the added hardship of a parent being diagnosed with cancer.

I was living two hours away from home at the time, and that turned out to be a blessing and a curse. It was so challenging and emotionally taxing to be physically distant from my parents and brothers during that time. I wanted so badly to be there for them at any moment. I wanted to be able to come over at the drop of a hat and just be present, but the hundred miles between us didn't allow for those spontaneous visits.

Although the distance didn't allow me to experience the "every day" of life with cancer, I think in some ways, that was a gift. I'm not sure if I could have stayed upright or continued to teach had I been living any closer to home. Living far away allowed me to compartmentalize my emotions and responsibilities and gave me the opportunity to escape the heaviness of the situation. I was grateful to only be a car ride away so I could come home on the weekends to help or just spend time with Mom, but those drives were also agonizing. Each time I left home, I would wonder if that was the last time that I'd see her.

The first time I saw my mom after receiving that horrific phone call is a vivid memory burned in my mind that still brings a lump to my throat even now as I write. I remember picking up flowers on my way to the hospital in hopes that they might lift her spirits even a little bit. Walking to the ICU felt like something out of a movie. It didn't feel real—like everything was happening in slow motion. As the automatic glass doors slid open, beckoning me to enter my mom's hallway, I took a deep breath and a step forward. Almost instantaneously, a nurse greeted me with a sharp tone and a sense of urgency. "Hey! You can't have those in here," she said, looking at the flowers in my hand. I froze. The lump in my throat tripled in size and I couldn't speak. "No fresh flowers are allowed in the ICU."

> WALKING TO THE ICU FELT LIKE SOMETHING OUT OF A MOVIE. IT DIDN'T FEEL REAL—LIKE EVERYTHING WAS HAPPENING IN SLOW MOTION.

The tears just started flowing from my eyes, and I was unable to stop them. The nurse must have been surprised by my response, because her voice softened, and she asked which patient I intended to visit. I still couldn't speak. It felt like she was seizing the one broken piece of hope I had left. Thankfully, my brother Liam had seen me walk in and headed in my direction to show me to Mom's room. He arrived by my side in time to answer the nurse's question, and he asked if we could just show the flowers to our mom and then take them back to the car. She agreed to that, and I took a moment to collect myself.

From the doorway, I caught a glimpse of her, and it took my breath away. There she was, my mom, the woman I described as "Superwoman" to those who didn't know her, lying in a hospital bed connected to so many different machines, her very breath assisted by the oxygen tube hooked gently around her ears and resting above her upper lip. I'm honestly not sure how I remained upright. Seeing the woman who had been the epitome of strength in my life now look so weak and fragile was like being pummeled by a fifty-foot ocean wave. It felt like I had been knocked over and tossed around under the forcefulness of the waters as I struggled to resurface for even a gasp of air.

She turned her head in my direction and we made eye contact. At that moment, I realized that she was the one who had been knocked over and that I was somehow supposed to be the strong one for her. I smiled big. "Hi, Mom!" I said. "It's so good to see you! I brought you these flowers, but I guess we can't have them in here, so they'll be on the counter at home awaiting your arrival."

The corners of her mouth moved upward ever so slightly to let me know that she appreciated the gesture, but it was clear that her weariness was preventing her from mustering up a full smile. I sat down in a chair next to her hospital bed, but the rest of the afternoon felt like a blur.

The next morning, I arrived at the hospital with a bag of Mom's makeup and a few things to do her hair. Today was the day we were going to make her feel like herself again. She sat up in her hospital bed, and we chatted as I put her makeup on. She seemed stronger today, and being able to just carry on a conversation with her was a relief. It felt like a slice of normalcy even though we were in a hospital room. I washed her hair and began to blow-dry it. As I watched her hair move slowly through the bristles of that round brush, I was once again pummeled by that ocean wave. It suddenly occurred to me that this could very well be one of the last times I'd be able to do this for her. I tried to swallow the sadness stuck in my throat as I pushed away the image of my mom without hair, refusing to believe she could ever be that sick. I moved the brush through her hair even more gently for fear that I might be the one to pull out a clump of it.

When I was finished, I gave her a mirror to see what she thought. Sure, she had some comments about the makeup, but she was so grateful. I think for a moment—just a moment—she forgot she was sick. She was reminded of who she was outside of these four walls and before "I have cancer" was ever even a thought in her head. The moment may have been fleeting, but I saw the spark in her eye revealing to me the fight she had left in her.

A few days later, Mom was moved out of the ICU and into a regular hospital room. She was resting after a spinal tap procedure (intrathecal chemotherapy) when the nurse came up with the first round of chemo that would be administered in the port in her chest. The lights were off in her room, and only the glow of the lights from the hallway swept in. My dad and I stood next to her bed as the nurse prepared the treatment. Dad reached out his hand and held Mom's as he fell to his knees. I rested my hand on top of his, and the buzz of the outside world seemed to fade into silence. Tears poured down my face. I couldn't stop them. I just stood there feeling so helpless as I wept and prayed, wishing I could take this all away or switch places with her. We remained there for quite some time even after the nurse departed, neither one of us saying anything aloud but both praying fervently for the woman we loved so dearly.

That moment is a treasured memory for me. Although it is painful and I still get choked up at the thought of it, I can recognize the beauty of that moment. Our hearts may have been gripped with fear, unable to even fathom the difficulty of the journey that lay ahead, but we had a moment of stillness and a breath of hope as we placed our trust in God. We prayed that every drop of medicine would find its perfect place.

Our story has a happy ending—or rather, our story is continuing to be written—and I thank God for that every single day. I realize that not everyone else receives this gift and that I've done nothing to merit such a gift, but what I can tell you is this:

Our God is good, and He is faithful. No matter your situation, He sees you. He hears you. He can handle your anger and your fear. He holds every single one of the tears you've shed. He has cried with you each time you allowed the grief within you to fall from your eyes, and He longs, just like you, for the day when there will be no more sorrow, no more pain. Until that day, we must place ourselves into His loving care and trust that He can and will bring good from every situation in our lives.

OUR GOD IS GOOD, AND HE IS FAITHFUL. NO MATTER YOUR SITUATION, HE CAN HANDLE YOUR ANGER AND YOUR FEAR.

ILLUMINATIONS

Maybe you're reading this and do not consider yourself a person of faith. Let me ask you this: Do you have faith in any area of your life? When you go to bed at night, do you count on the sun to rise the next morning? Do you expect to live another day? When you get into your car, do you suppose it will bring you from point A to point B? When you take ibuprofen for your headache, do you anticipate the relief of your pain? I could go on, but I think you get my point.

My suspicion is that in some area of your life, you do have faith. You do put your trust in some*body* or some*thing* outside of yourself. So now let me ask you this: What do you have to lose by putting that trust in God? From my standpoint, I do not think there is any loss, only gain. I would invite you to be open to creating space in your life for God. Maybe today is the first day you've ever prayed, or maybe it's been years or even decades since you've done so. Whatever situation you're in, know that God, who is Love itself, anxiously awaits your conversation. He earnestly desires to shower you with good and beautiful things and is ready to give you the grace and strength to endure your trials.

I don't tell you this because I read it in a book somewhere and think it's a nice message or a sweet thing to say. I tell you this because it is my lived experience. I know for a fact that I would not have been able to survive my mom's cancer diagnosis except through the grace of God, and I hope and pray that you, too, will be open to experience the tender care of our Heavenly Father.

In addition to faith, the gift of community was so important in helping us through the long days of life with cancer. We were (and are) so fortunate to have so many family members and friends who were willing to help us in whatever way we needed. If you are reading this as a friend of someone who has had a traumatic diagnosis, ask their family members how they are holding up. I had a friend in college—let's call her Maria—whose mom was going through treatment for ovarian cancer after a bout with breast cancer just a few years earlier. I remember asking her one day what it was like to have a parent go through cancer and expressing that it must just be so hard. I asked her how she was doing. She began to cry. "Everyone always asks, 'How's your mom doing?' which is great, and I appreciate that, but like . . . what about me? I'm over here falling apart, and no one ever says, 'How are *you* doing, Maria?'"

It might seem too easy or even trivial to simply ask, "Hey, how are you doing?" to a family member or caregiver, but when asked with genuine care, that question can go a long way. Now, they might not answer the question honestly or want to talk for too long (or even at all), but they will appreciate that you gave them space to do so. If they share, just listen. They know you can't solve it or cure it. Just give them space to release the weight of what they've been holding on to, and then be as empathetic as you possibly can. If you feel so inclined, maybe take them out for a cup of coffee or lunch. Send them a card or a small gift. Obviously, the person going through treatment needs those uplifting notes and little gifts to keep going, but the caregivers appreciate those things too. It's nice when others recognize that the diagnosis goes beyond the patient. Those close to the patient—be they family members or close friends—carry so many emotions and fears on behalf of their loved one. Offering your support to the caregivers and family will encourage them and help them to persevere. People are generally supportive when the news first hits, but as time wears on, the kind words, notes, or gifts trail off. Consider sending a card or gift, making a phone call, or scheduling a time for lunch at the beginning, then set a reminder in your phone to do it again a month or two down the road. The *consistent* presence of community can never be underestimated.

My hope is that this book is a helpful resource for you in your own journey. I hope that you gain insight and feel a sense of solidarity as you read it. May you know that you are never alone in the hardship, pain, or fear that comes with a traumatic diagnosis. Be assured of my prayers for you and your loved ones as you navigate this path.

A VISIT FROM RILEY

Journal Entry by Britta McKenna
March 19, 2016

Riley went on a road trip from the McKennas to return home for a visit at Mo's request. He performed his happy dance to eagerly say hello to his family. Riley's little tail stub was a waggin', and he brought comfort that only a dog can. There was more strength in Mo's voice today as she had a "better day" in her words. A home visit by the physical therapist had Mo doing some strengthening exercises and timed walking paths in the house. Nothing like a stopwatch to get Mo's competitive juices flowing!

Tonight, the family celebrated Sean's birthday (which was, appropriately on St. Paddy's Day). That's all for now as things at home seem calm—all our angel prayers are working their magic, so keep them coming!

PART

2

EXTENDED FAMILY

AS POINTS OF LIGHT

Family is everything to me. That started with my parents, Bill and Helen Vernal. They taught us that friends will come and go, but your family is forever. I know this to be true.

None of our extended family lives in the same state. Can you imagine? All of them had to travel to see me, be with me, help me. Each gift meant a flight, a long drive, hours of commitment. But they all did it without hesitation. The gift. Family.

A great toll was placed on my extended family: the worry, the feeling of distance and helplessness. How could they participate? How could they bring joy? The answer is that they all *did* participate. They brought joy. They helped me back to wholeness. Simply by being. Simply by showing up.

There is no single way to help. But they all did what they could when they could. And it made all the difference.

CHAPTER 6
KAREN VERNAL
MAUREEN'S SISTER

*Since our mom passed away in 2016, Karen has assumed the role of the matriarch of our family. The oldest of four, she is also the one who drives our connection. Karen is reflective, prayerful, and contemplative, and she has experienced great life tragedies of her own. She taught me about resilience through those tragedies. Karen also taught me about **"alternative ways of healing,"** as she will share with you. Karen researched therapies outside of Western medicine, which I'm convinced contributed to my well-being and health.*

It was February 2016. The days were gray and heavy.

Maureen and I talk regularly, so when I learned that after weeks of pain in her shoulder, she was going to have an MRI to determine whether she had torn her rotator cuff, I was relieved.

And I wasn't prepared. I wasn't prepared to hear her say "lymphoma." Cancer. I felt dizzy. I felt like I was in one of those carnival fun houses where mirrors distorted all the images. Everything in my reality felt distorted. All I knew was that I needed to be with Maureen. She agreed that I could join her and Dan when they were to meet with the oncologist.

February 25, 2016. Tom (my husband) and I drove to the hospital, arriving before Maureen and Dan. As we sat in the waiting area, Maureen and Dan came through the front door. I hardly recognized her. She looked frail (a foreign description for her) and shaky on her feet. Despondent. Her voice was a whisper. It was hard for me to breathe. I tried to remain calm even as I went into the examining room with Maureen and Dan to meet with Dr. Bayer.

I held tight, willing myself not to pass out or scream as I saw the MRI results on the screen. There were multiple tumors (shoulders, neck, back, legs). I kept telling myself to breathe. Just breathe.

> I HAVE LEARNED, HAVING BEEN WITH MANY FRIENDS RECEIVING CRITICAL MEDICAL INFORMATION, HOW IMPORTANT IT IS TO HAVE SOMEONE THERE TO TAKE NOTES.

My role in that meeting was to take notes. I have learned, having been with many friends receiving critical medical information, how important it is to have someone there to take notes. As a patient, spouse, or significant other, it is too hard to take in and remember all that one might be told during these consultation meetings. I remember that in some way, taking notes helped me to feel grounded. I was also breathless writing the words: "stage 4 diffuse large B-cell non-Hodgkin's lymphoma. Aggressive. Fast growing."

Breathe, Karen, breathe.

During my prayers in the days and weeks to come, these words came: "Courage doesn't mean you don't get afraid. Courage means you don't let fear stop you." Please, God, I prayed. And it didn't! It didn't stop Maureen, and it didn't stop those of us who love her.

Cancer or any life-threatening disease is a family affair. I was the one to call my sister, Patricia, and my brother, Bill. They were both stunned and ready to support. Patricia came at once, and she stayed for ten days. She had the challenge of being both sister and medical professional, researching treatment options, consulting with Maureen's doctors, and supporting Dan and their kids with her knowledge and care. She remained vigilant throughout, maintaining long-distance communication with doctors through email and phone.

> *COURAGE DOESN'T MEAN YOU DON'T GET AFRAID. COURAGE MEANS YOU DON'T LET FEAR STOP YOU.*

Bill was "on call" for whatever Maureen and Dan might need from him. He checked in regularly.

Some people close the doors and windows and manage their diagnosis alone. Maureen taught us that it is OK to ask for and receive help. I don't think that was easy for her. She was used to being the caregiver in the lives of so many friends. We needed to call on all our angels in heaven and on earth to support us, to love us through the trials of fear and unknowing, because as caregivers, we also needed care. We opened a wide circle of love and prayer and healing, from one end of the country to the other . . . and we invited relatives and friends from Germany and Ireland to join their spirits with ours. The prayerful energy of this community of care was palpable.

As a first step in her treatment, Maureen needed to have hip surgery to secure a fracture so that she would be able to walk during chemotherapy. Tom and I returned to Batavia to offer support to Maureen and Dan and family. When we showed up, we brought snacks and drinks and anything we thought might offer comfort. When in doubt, bring food!

In early March, Maureen began her regime of chemotherapy. She went into Northwestern Hospital for six rounds. That meant that for five days, twenty-four hours a day, she received a continuous chemo cocktail. Then there were two weeks of reprieve at home, recovering for the next hospital round. But even on those in-between days, she had to go to the hospital every day for a shot to boost her blood count. Most mornings during that entire time, I sent Maureen a daily meditation or quote or picture of inspiration, hope, or humor, and each time she was hospitalized, I went to stay with her for a night or two. Definitely on Thursday. Thursdays were our overnight stays together.

Dan was adamant that Maureen would not be left alone while she was in the hospital. He was right! There were times when whoever was there could respond to her needs at the moment, whether that was help to the bathroom, a glass of ice water, or a comforting hand to hold.

I remember vividly, that after the first round of chemotherapy, when Maureen ended up with the flu and pneumonia and needed to return to the hospital. When I walked into her room, she had makeup on and hair/wig in place. (Of course she did!) She was in bed, fully covered to her neck. I went to her and held her.

I remember Maureen asking, "Why can't there be more holding?"

That continues to be a mystery for me. Our need for tender touch, aside from the necessary medical interventions, is clearly a contributing factor to healing.

I think one of the roles that I played for Maureen and in our family was and is to look for alternative healing sources. I had learned from a friend who had gone through chemotherapy that icing hands and feet can prevent neuropathy. I found spa booties and mittens that we kept refreshed with ice packs for Maureen. I had also learned that ice can prevent hair loss and that Germany's health care had been using cooling caps since the seventies. While Maureen did not elect to use an ice cap, we did use gel packs for her eyes to save her eyebrows. The medical professionals were curious, if not a bit skeptical, yet Maureen was willing!

Another alternative that I discovered was aromatherapy. I contacted a woman who had studied aromatherapy after serving as a nurse for twenty-five years. Barbara was able to tell me about the essential oils that would be particularly beneficial to Maureen. Frankincense was one of the oils that Barb recommended we use on Maureen's feet. (Applying it had the added benefit of touch and foot massage.) We also had lavender in a diffuser in Maureen's room. It was quite telling when nurses would come to Maureen's room during their break to experience the soothing relaxation of the incense. Why that isn't an option in most health care settings, I don't know.

Western medicine can be so limiting unless someone on the care team is willing to go outside of the usual box! I suppose that was also a role for me as we all made our way through the grief and stress of Maureen's illness, praying for the outcome that we hoped for even as she suffered through the pain and fear of multiple treatments.

Of course, there were so many unanticipated surprises . . .

During round two, for example, Maureen was feeling OK. I was with her for two days and offered to get some "real" food for dinner one evening. A favorite nurse recommended Houlihan's.

Maureen decided that she'd like either the stuffed chicken or the meat loaf dinner. When I asked for advice from the receptionist at the restaurant about the two options, telling her I was ordering dinner for my sister who was in the hospital, she asked, "Why is she hospitalized?" I took a deep breath and said, "Lymphoma. She has lymphoma. And she is going through several rounds of five full days of chemotherapy at a time."

She immediately responded, "The meat loaf. I've learned that when people go through chemotherapy, their sense of smell is diminished, and while the chicken is delicious, the smell of the meat loaf is stronger." Meat loaf it was then, and several times after!

About ten minutes later, a man came out with our order. Shaking my hand, he said, "My name is Gary Smith. I am the manager here. I want you to know that I am very sorry about your sister. If there is anything we can do to help, we will. And with your permission, I would like to include both of you in my prayers. "Do you mind telling me what kind of cancer?"

"Stage 4 lymphoma," I said.

He said, "Me too."

You can imagine my shock and wonder and gratitude that standing right in front of me was a man who had survived this horrible disease himself. He shared that unlike Maureen, his cancer was slow growing. He had had several treatments over the course of two years and was to have another round beginning in May.

When our dinner was ready, I went to hand him my credit card. Gary said, "No, this is on us." And that continued to be true for the rest of the time Maureen went through treatment and we had our Thursday night meat loaf dinner ritual together.

Miracles came from strangers. Meeting Gary gave me hope. He was living a full life. Maureen could have that possibility in front of her too. Gary Smith modeled compassion, empathy, generosity, and a desire to serve. In so many ways, he mirrored Maureen's spirit. It surely wasn't about the free meal for us that was so healing for me and for Maureen. It was the experience of a stranger offering an uncommon act of kindness with authenticity and humility.

One of the many ways that Maureen engaged with those who love her and supported her during this time was her engagement through CaringBridge. She had the opportunity to track her experience and to express gratitude, and those who love her could respond within this online platform.

Britta McKenna, Maureen's dear friend, set up the Caring-Bridge website for us. Britta became a sister. She did so much to invite support for Maureen and Dan and the kids. She organized meals, kept people informed, visited regularly, arranged for Maureen's garden to be planted, and so much more. I remember that she and Jan O'Brien, Maureen's sister-in-love, were often the leaders in direct external care. The nurses all fell in love with Maureen and welcomed us generously. I earned the nickname "Joy" by the nursing staff. If truth be told, I know that Maureen appreciated my humor and my antics! JOY and HUMOR go hand in hand in healing, and I was grateful to bring both.

While supporting Maureen in the best ways I knew how, I was also supporting our mother, who was in memory care near our home in Wauwatosa, Wisconsin. I knew that I needed to talk with Mom about Maureen's illness and treatment.

It was St. Patrick's Day when I sat with Mom and told her of Maureen's illness. While I did not offer all the details of Maureen's illness, she was visibly alarmed. She said, "We need to get her to a hospital right now." She felt better knowing that Maureen was *in* the hospital. "What can we do?" she asked.

"We can pray, Mom," I said.

And so I held her hands and we prayed the prayer that was etched in her heart . . . a mother's prayer: "Hail Mary." I then suggested that she could write a message to Maureen. I would take a picture and send it to Maureen that day.

> WE CANNOT CONTROL OUTCOMES. WE CAN SIMPLY TRUST THAT LOVE MAKES A DIFFERENCE.

Mom carefully wrote the words, "I love you! And that's enough," on the page. That's it, isn't it? That is what we can do for one another. We cannot control outcomes. We can simply trust that love makes a difference. Love heals. Love invites us into the unknown to live with courage. As Bethany Hamilton said after losing an arm to a shark, "Courage doesn't mean you are not afraid. Courage means that you will not let fear stop you."

And *love*. Love made a difference for Maureen. Love made a difference for each of us in her wide circle, and none of us will ever be the same. I think that each of us lives with a deeper appreciation of life and a greater understanding of the importance of living life to the fullest.

On the last day that Maureen was hospitalized, I helped to organize a surprise parade. So much fun! So much excitement! We had balloons, a Superwoman costume, cape, and crown for Maureen. My brother, Bill, and his wife, Kathy, flew in to surprise and celebrate. All of Maureen's kids were there—Liam,

CJ, Sean, and Lizzy—plus dozens of friends, all with hats, kazoos, banners, and songs!

Nurses and staff, friends and family filled the halls as Maureen left. Hugs. Tears. Cheers. The impossible became possible! **Love wins.**

ILLUMINATIONS

Breathe. It's important to take time for yourself along the way as you provide support for a loved one.
Take notes. The sheer amount of information covered in a single meeting can be overwhelming, and offering to keep a record of what information was covered and what decisions were made is extraordinarily helpful.

When in doubt, bring food! Grieving families always appreciate having one less thing to worry about after a long and difficult day.

Think outside the box. Ice caps and aromatherapy may not be taught in medical school, but that doesn't mean they can't be beneficial to the recipient—and they facilitate more touch, which is beneficial on its own!

Love. It makes a difference. It heals.

BACK TO THE HOSPITAL WE GO

Journal Entry by Britta McKenna

March 23, 2016

Yesterday was a bad day for Mo: nausea, vomiting, weakness, fever. Her description to me was "Ugh." This morning's visit to the cancer center for her shot and check in with Dr. Bayer resulted in her being sent to the ER and then to be admitted. Mo's counts are low with not much to fight the infection, so she'll remain in the hospital for a couple of days to receive fluids and medications through her port. Lizzy is spending the night so Dan can rest. The marathon continues. Calling on all our prayer warriors for the long haul.

GOOD FRIDAY, NOT SO GOOD FRIDAY

Journal Entry by Britta McKenna

March 25, 2016

Today Maureen is now battling flu and pneumonia along with a 104.4 degree fever. She remains in the hospital and the family requests no visitors at this time and no flowers. Please check Caringbridge for updates instead of calling or texting the family. The family appreciates all of your concern and asks to keep the prayers coming. If you'd like to do something, here are a few ideas:

Drop a card in the mail to the family and insert a gift card for a healthy meal choice (Boston Market, Panera, Corner Bakery) that they can use while going to and from the hospital or nights when they are on the run. Sign up to deliver a ready to eat meal to their home on a M-W-F at Mealtrain. Ellen Ball has opened up the rest of April and May for those who can help here.

FEVER DOWN, SPIRITS UP

Journal Entry by Britta McKenna

March 26, 2016

This afternoon Maureen is surrounded by family with Lizzy, CJ, Sean, Aunt Karen and Tom gathered in her hospital room for a mini-Easter celebration. Mo's fever is down, and spirits are up. Amen!

COUNTS ARE UP!

Journal Entry by Britta McKenna

March 29, 2016

The good news is that Maureen's white counts are up (the infection fighters) from 1,000 to over 350,000. Perhaps all the prayer warriors are to thank for upping the counts. One prayer = 1,000 count (my rough estimation). Keep 'em coming! Mo is enjoying sister-in-law Jan's visit and had a good day today at home. One day at a time.

CHAPTER 7

PATRICIA VERNAL BURKHART, PHD

PROFESSOR AND ASSOCIATE DEAN EMERITA,
UNIVERSITY OF KENTUCKY; MAUREEN'S SISTER

> *My sister Patricia is always the resident on call. It must be so tough for her. Rarely does she get to be simply "wife, mother, daughter, sister, aunt." Our entire family looks to her as a health manual and expert anytime there is a health crisis. She never complains. She only obliges. She **"advocates as a health professional"** in every family health circumstance.*
>
> *It was no different with me. She spoke the language of the doctors and could explain in laypersons' terms what they were saying. I often had her read the results of scans or tests before I did. I know it was a heavy burden for her. I am grateful.*

Every day is a gift. This was a phrase my husband and I frequently repeated while raising our two sons, now adults. Our youngest son had severe asthma with frequent hospitalizations, so we lived this phrase, grateful for every easy, unlabored breath. On February 26, 2016, this phrase took on new meaning when I received a call from my older sister, Karen, that Maureen (our younger sister) was diagnosed with lymphoma and would require immediate surgery to stabilize her cancer-invaded hip. This surgery would occur prior to embarking on aggressive chemotherapy to treat the widespread cancer. These words took my breath away; the world stopped. The bond between sisters is fierce, and so was my determination that everything was going to be OK!

I am a health care professional. My first thought was, "We need another opinion *before* beginning any treatment, since Maureen likely would get only one shot at a successful outcome."

Today is a gift: I need to help Maureen fight with every available tool. During the call, I told Karen I needed to talk with Maureen's doctor about the recommended treatment plan and seek another expert opinion prior to beginning the treatment. As a PhD-prepared nursing professor and a researcher, I knew there were National Institutes of Health (NIH) cancer centers that had ongoing clinical trials and evidence-based, cutting-edge cancer treatments. I knew my own university, where I was an associate dean, had an NIH cancer center. I wanted Maureen's diagnosis and treatment plan to be reviewed at one of these centers.

I do not live in Illinois where Maureen is located. My home is in Kentucky, and at the time of her diagnosis, I was presenting a research paper at a conference in Williamsburg, Virginia. From my hotel room and with permission of Maureen and her husband, I placed a call to the doctor overseeing Maureen's current health care. I had a list of questions and concerns about Maureen's diagnosis, treatment, prognosis, survival rate, and, most importantly, how I could best support her. My primary goal was focused on obtaining a second opinion for my sister's case from an NIH cancer center. We just had to be sure of the diagnosis and the best plan of action before my sister began the life-saving treatment. Thankfully, the doctor responded to my call. I had several questions written on the hotel room's tablet: *Is a lymph node biopsy being done to confirm the diagnosis? What is the prognosis and survival rate? What is the treatment plan? Are there successful evidence-based treatments or ongoing clinical trials in which Maureen would be eligible to participate?* And most importantly, *Will the doctor help us secure a second opinion at an NIH cancer center?*

The doctor compassionately answered each of my questions and provided evidence-based data to support what he was recommending. He confirmed the diagnosis of diffuse large B-cell lymphoma, stage 4, which is advanced cancer in several areas of the body. He acknowledged that the immediate plan was to do a lymph node biopsy that day to confirm the diagnosis, then to insert a med port, a small tube inserted beneath the skin into a vein of the upper chest, for delivery of the chemotherapeutic medicine. The chemotherapy was to occur every three to four weeks for six to eight cycles. The doctor affirmed that during each of these full-week cycles of chemotherapy, Maureen would need to be hospitalized.

The doctor also advised that an orthopedic surgeon would perform surgery on her hip that night to stabilize it so that Maureen could get up to walk following surgery, helping to prevent postoperative complications such as pneumonia. Three to four days following the hip surgery, my sister would be discharged to her home. After a short recovery period, chemotherapy would begin, and it would be aggressive. The doctor acknowledged that this type of cancer is fast growing, but there was every indication the cancer would respond to the recommended treatment.

He agreed to a second opinion and suggested a lymphoma specialist at the University of Chicago, an NIH cancer center.

My last question was, *How can I best support Maureen at this time?* Without wavering, the doctor's voice on the phone said, "I recommend you come as soon as you possibly can." Clearly, he was signaling the extent of the emotional toll this health care crisis was creating for my sister. I began to wonder incredulously how Maureen's early complaint of moderate shoulder pain could have led to an unexpected diagnosis of cancer, an extensive aggressive treatment plan, and immediate hip surgery. *How could this be? Is the diagnosis accurate?*

My mind was racing about how best to get to Illinois immediately. From my hotel room, I called my husband, who jumped into action, booking a flight for me from Virginia back home to Kentucky to unpack and repack, followed by a flight to Illinois, where I stayed with Maureen for the next ten days.

TODAY IS A GIFT. HOW DO WE PROTECT IT?

My emotions vacillated between those of a competent health professional and a shell-shocked sister. *How did this happen? How can we fix it? How do we get this behind us? What can I do to most effectively ensure my sister's successful health outcome and, at the same time, support her as my sister? Today is a gift . . . how do we protect it?*

When I arrived at the Illinois community hospital the next morning, Maureen was lying in a bed in the intensive care unit with her husband and oldest son by her side. The orthopedic surgeon had placed a stabilizing rod in her cancer-ridden hip the night before. It is hard to describe my emotions at that time. My sister looked pale as she lay very still in the hospital bed. I positioned myself in the tilt-back chair beside her to spend the night and sent her exhausted family home to sleep. Teasing, I told my sister that my rates as a PhD nurse were considerable, but I would give her the family discount! We had a few laughs and a few cries that night. The journey to regain the *gift* of health had begun.

Maureen was discharged a few days later. The next week was grueling for my sister. She experienced considerable hip pain after the surgery, and she was learning how to walk with that pain and simultaneously preparing for upcoming chemotherapy. Her four adult children so wanted to do something for their mother, *anything*. There was so much to do. *Where do we start?*

I decided to use my experience as a nurse manager and dean to assign specific tasks to each of her three sons. Liam, her oldest son, oversaw the multitude of meals coming from neighbors and friends and made sure the dishwasher was emptied each day. Sean, son #3, ran errands, picking up medical supplies and prescriptions. I asked CJ (#2) to organize into folders any medical bills that needed to be paid, filed, or forwarded to the insurance company. Maureen's youngest child and only daughter, Elizabeth (Lizzy), was empathetic and "hands on." She watched carefully how I assisted her mother to walk each day: first sitting up, then standing next to the bed, followed by walking around the first floor of the house assisted with a walker. Elizabeth did it just that way. She loved spending time with her mom, and Maureen brightened each weekend that her daughter came to stay. Maureen had nine medications she was required to take daily or as needed (e.g., pain medication). We downloaded a medication flow sheet like that used by the hospital, and with my help, Elizabeth set up a medication schedule, labeling each bottle and time of administration.

Each of her children demonstrated extraordinary love and concern for their mother. Her husband, Dan, soldiered on, ensuring that decisions were made in a timely manner. He was an early riser each day to keep his job going and resolute that Maureen was not to be left alone. Dan was loving and kind with Maureen, introspective and prayerful in his own grief, and unwavering in his determination that Maureen's health would be restored.

With my sister's permission, I exchanged several emails with the consulting lymphoma specialist, Dr. Sonali Smith, at the University of Chicago Medicine Comprehensive Cancer Center, where Maureen had an appointment scheduled several days following her hip surgery. Dr. Smith was one of the most knowledgeable, competent, thorough, kind, and responsive health providers I had the privilege of meeting. I continued to have email contact with Dr. Smith throughout the course of Maureen's treatment. She always responded. There were even times when I questioned procedures or treatments the local doctor was recommending, and Dr. Smith agreed to intervene. This took enormous pressure off the shoulders of the family. This doctor immediately became the "quarterback" of my sister's health care team. What a blessing!

For the first scheduled appointment, Dr. Smith required that we bring Maureen's actual tests, not just the reports. This would allow her to analyze the results herself. Prior to the appointment, I spent many days on the phone securing slides, scans, X-rays, and other materials to take with us to the appointment. Once I contacted the hospital or laboratory and was able to speak directly with a supervisor who could authorize the release of the medical data, one of Maureen's sons would volunteer to retrieve them. Securing every test was a tedious process, but on the day of the appointment with the consulting lymphoma specialist at the University of Chicago, we hand-carried all the requested data into the meeting.

My full-time position as a university nursing professor and associate dean kept me mostly in Kentucky. However, after the first ten-day leave of absence from my work to be with Maureen during the initial days following her cancer diagnosis, I went back to be with her six more times. My role became one of crisis intervention, timing these trips when crucial health decisions were being made, a new treatment was to begin, or important appointments with health providers occurred that would determine next steps. I yearned to be there for the celebrations of small moments of success, but I knew I was needed most when my health care expertise would be beneficial.

IT WAS PARALYZING TO WAIT FOR THE RESULTS, THEN TO LOG ON TO HER CHART, AND HOPE FOR THE BEST.

I talked with Maureen or one of her family members daily. Each day was an update on Maureen's progress and emotional health. Maureen asked me to sign in to her electronic record so that I could see the results of chemotherapy and scans indicating the shrinking of the tumors. This was both a blessing and a curse. The doctors were monitoring a lab blood level frequently to indicate whether the cancer was being eradicated by the chemotherapy. Once the blood was drawn, Maureen would call me to ask me to monitor the results and share them with her. Each time I logged on, I prayed I could share good news with her. It was paralyzing to wait for the results, then to log on to her chart and hope for the best. Fortunately, the treatment was highly effective.

I was in Illinois with Maureen following one of her six chemotherapy treatments. She was awaiting the lab results and a body scan. When the results showed up on the electronic chart, Maureen insisted that I review them and tell her what they indicated. She went to sit outside, soaking in the sunshine and praying, while I sat at her computer. I carefully read and reread the electronic chart. The blood level and scan indicated the tumors had diminished considerably, but there were still indications of the cancer. I was elated that the results suggested the treatment was working effectively and the cancer was receding. I danced out onto the patio to announce the good news. My sister erupted into giant sobs, completely decimated by the update. Her hope was that the tests would reveal she was cancer-free and required no further treatment. While I was elated, she was devastated. We cried together, and then we both danced on the patio.

Such waves of emotion through a health care crisis: grief, devastation, elation, and hope. But here is the good news: my sister is now *cancer-free* almost five years after the diagnosis. A roller coaster ride, for sure.

Every day is a gift—and Maureen's gift of health has been restored. We are blessed!

ILLUMINATIONS

Clearly, there are lessons we learned from this experience about how to stand with a loved one experiencing a health crisis.

Standing with a Loved One

Maureen's job was to fight this horrific disease with all her might: to be a warrior. She was an incredible warrior! Maureen was strong, resilient, and resolute in her determination to beat this disease. Our job, as Maureen's family and friends, was to stand with her, offering support and strength.

The support a family member or friend who is a health professional can offer to a loved one living through a health crisis is advocacy. If you are lucky enough to have friends or family members in the health profession, you can ask them to accompany you to doctor appointments, treatments, or hospitalizations. These health professionals can be the note-takers and can ask appropriate questions on your behalf. This professional advocacy can be critical to the successful outcome of a health crisis.

My health care advocacy for my sister began several months prior to her diagnosis. When I talked with her over the Christmas holiday (long before the February diagnosis), she told me about persistent pain in her shoulder that was not relieved with ibuprofen. With my health professional hat on, I suggested that if the pain and lack of mobility did not resolve in a few days, she should seek medical attention. That occurred. The doctor prescribed an X-ray (results were negative) followed by physical therapy. The adeptness and advocacy of the physical therapist, who raised the alarm about the extent of Maureen's pain and lack of arm mobility, fueled further tests, resulting in the diagnosis and referral to an oncologist.

I watched each nurse who cared for Maureen in the hospital advocate on her behalf. The consulting cancer specialist advocated on Maureen's behalf to ensure the most efficacious, evidence-based treatment. The doctor caring for Maureen was willing to work with the consulting doctor outside of his health system to ensure Maureen received the treatment plan that would result in the best outcomes. The advocacy of the physical therapist, doctors, and nurses who treated my sister cannot be underestimated. They shared their expertise courageously and compassionately.

As a university nursing professor, I routinely tell my students what a privilege it is to be able to care for patients during their most vulnerable times. Health professionals truly are in a unique position to make a difference in patients' lives every single day, providing competent, compassionate care and often courageous advocacy.

As a family member who is a health care professional, I was in a unique position to question the course of Maureen's treatment, support her inpatient and post-hospital care, take careful notes during the visits of various doctors involved in her care, and decipher for her and her family what they had said. It's a fine line we walk: health professional and family member. There were times when, providing care to my sister, my heart ached for her. Sometimes I just wanted to be her sister and hold her tightly, but I knew the expertise I brought to the situation was needed. I navigated these roles by assessing the need each day. Some days we were just sisters, laughing and talking together as sisters do. Other days I functioned in the role of the nurse or advocate for her care. I knew her husband could rest peacefully if I were with Maureen, and so I stayed at her bedside. Sometimes I gave her a bath, administered medicine, or helped her to walk. Occasionally, I just needed to take a walk outside myself!

Being Present in the Moment and Bringing Joy

So many people in Maureen's community of care were filled with loving support. In their own ways, they shared their talents and kindness, making meals, running errands, praying, regularly emailing or calling, sending cards, planting flowers, and planning celebrations for treatment milestones. Many have shared their stories in this book.

When I was with Maureen, I tried to keep the tone light and fun or just be present with whatever feeling was her emotion of the day. The most inspiring "presence" I observed was that of her husband and children. As a remembrance of this life-altering experience, I bought Maureen's husband a Superman costume but called it "Super Elmer." Without a doubt, Dan was the glue that held the family together through this difficult time. He was unwavering in his insistence that Maureen never is left alone. Each of the children regularly came to help, be present, and bring joy to their mother. Friends and neighbors chipped in, doing whatever was needed. It was a team effort.

What We Learned about Becoming a Community of Care

So, what did we learn from this experience that might help others support a friend or family member experiencing a significant health crisis? Most notable to me was that *everyone* has something to offer.

Advocacy of health professionals.

If you are a health professional, standing with someone you care about can manifest itself as courageously advocating on their behalf. Nurses, doctors, physical therapists, or other health experts should never underestimate the unique contributions they make to their patients' successful physical and emotional health. Health care professionals can make a difference every single day by the competent, compassionate care they provide and by courageously advocating on behalf of their patients.

Being present in the moment and bringing joy.
Friends can offer something as simple as shoveling the driveway, putting away trash cans, or making a meal. (One small piece of advice: if you do make a meal, be certain you send it in a disposable or nonreturnable container. Otherwise, someone in the circle of family and friends has the job of returning the dish.)

If you have a green thumb, you might consider planting flowers or positioning potted plants outside a sick person's window. You can offer to run errands for prescriptions, medical supplies, or groceries. Something as simple as a card or email sent at frequent intervals will let loved ones know you are thinking of them.

One last thing: don't forget to offer support to the other family members. Maureen's husband and children were grieving too. It was so difficult for them to witness the grueling treatments Maureen endured. When someone acknowledged this, it brought great comfort to Maureen's family. Something as simple as neighbors gathering outside of the family's home for a candlelight vigil, just to let the family know they are thinking of and praying for them, is powerfully meaningful.

Every day is a gift! If you are lucky enough to have the gift of good health, celebrate it. If you know someone who is suffering through a health crisis, stand with them in any way you possibly can. It matters, and it is sacred to be part of a loved one's community of care.

STEADY STATE

Journal Entry by Britta McKenna

April 3, 2016

Mo is holding her own at home and resting up for the next round of chemo. This past week has had more ups than downs and an emotional moment when she said goodbye to her hair and hello to a nicely styled wig (thank you to Mariann Schira for the wonderful selection from ACS and LivingWell to choose from). The many cards and notes sustain her during this time when we ask for visitors to be kept at a minimum to avoid introducing germs. CJ is home visiting this weekend in between travels and ultimate frisbee competitions, sister-in-law, Jan is the day shift and Dan holds steadfast as her rock of support. Mo has an appointment with her doctor tomorrow and will hear more about her counts and status of when Round 2 will commence.

LOUD AND CLEAR

Journal Entry by Britta McKenna

April 5, 2016

Mo's trip to the doc was good news as her lung x-rays were clear! And to add to that good news was her green light to enjoy a glass of wine (if she wants). Food is tasting better, especially a big bowl of ice cream today. A solid night's sleep and a strong and determined voice made for a much better day.

Thank you to the dozens of prayer warriors who lift up Mo and her family. Keep it coming.

CHAPTER 8

BILL VERNAL

MAUREEN'S BROTHER

> *My brother Bill is the only boy in a family of girls. That couldn't have been easy. We often tease Bill that he was the favorite because his chore list was so much simpler than ours, but Bill's role then and now was not easy. I'm sure it was tough for him to learn that his only little sister was fighting for her life, states away.*
>
> *Bill will share with you the importance of* **"regularly touching base."** *While geography was not in our favor, Bill and his wife Kathy visited often, sent text messages on a regular basis, and worked hard to be present during our family's difficult journey.*

When Maureen asked me to contribute this book about her cancer diagnosis almost five years ago, my first thought was, *I can't remember what I had for lunch yesterday, never mind putting*

*into words what my thoughts and emotions were five years ago . . .
but I'll do my best.*

I remember getting a call from my sister Karen letting
us know that Maureen had gone to the doctor for an MRI
because she was having trouble with her shoulder. It was
then that they discovered she had a tumor in her shoulder,
and she was eventually diagnosed with stage 4 lymphoma.
Like everyone else, I was stunned. What exactly does that
mean? My only thought at that time was that I should call
my sister Patricia, our resident family medical expert, to get
some answers.

Patricia's response was not good. It was then that I knew
Maureen and the whole family had a big problem. What do
you do when you get that kind of news? I had no experience
dealing with something like this. The next day, I went to work
and asked a good friend who had lost his mother to cancer if he
had any thoughts on the situation. He gave me an answer that
I did not want to hear. He told me that I should prepare for the
worst because Maureen was in for a very tough road, and she
probably wouldn't make it.

> WHAT DO YOU DO WHEN YOU GET THAT
> KIND OF NEWS? I HAD NO EXPERIENCE
> DEALING WITH SOMETHING LIKE THIS.

After hearing that, I had to decide. How could I best help
this dreadful situation when Maureen was in Chicago and I
was in Florida? I decided to be as positive as I could by texting
positive thoughts through her chemotherapy treatments and
trying to visit as much as possible.

At the time, my mother was in a nursing home in Milwaukee with dementia/Alzheimer's disease. Since Milwaukee is only about two hours away from Chicago, I was able to visit Maureen a few times as she fought through her journey. I can remember two visits clearly.

The first was when I saw Maureen after she had lost all her hair. That's when it really hit me. Cancer is a real monster, and Maureen was going through hell. The second one was on her last chemo treatment. My wife Kathy and I flew out to Chicago to celebrate on her last day of her last of six rounds of chemo. She had done it! The entire hospital staff seemed to be in a celebratory, party mood. It was amazing to see the joy and happiness from everyone in our family and every single person who was part of the terrific staff at the hospital. It gave me a perspective that the world is a much better place than the media leads us to believe.

Unfortunately, just a year later, Kathy and I got to experience our own piece of hell when she was diagnosed with bladder cancer. We got a real sense of what Maureen went through when the doctor said those words: "You have cancer." Although the experience of having your only "little sister" have cancer was traumatic, I had it somewhat easier than the rest of my siblings because I was so far away. I didn't have constant reminders on a daily basis. When your life partner gets the news, it literally changes your life because your entire focus every minute of every day turns to ways to beat this disease. Kathy, like Maureen, has been blessed with a positive result. After three years of treatment, Kathy remains "cancer-free."

During these years of trials, tribulations, and treatments, it became very evident how much more difficult it is to experience cancer when you are part of an immediate family that must live with it every single day, all day. I certainly have a much better perspective on what Maureen and Dan and their family went through now that Kathy and I have lived in the same world.

ILLUMINATIONS

It's very difficult to try advising someone how to help or even react when a loved one gets such horrible news. Really, the only answer is to be positive and supportive and commit to being there whenever you're needed and/or able.

DAY OF REST

Journal Entry by Britta McKenna
April 10, 2016

Mo is resting up at home with family and has been feeling stronger these past few days. Tomorrow morning, she reports back to the hospital to start Round 2 chemo and she is ready! Mo is scheduled to be in the hospital for 5 days for her chemo protocol.

Dan and the family thank everyone for the encouraging cards and posts, gifts, tasty meals and gift cards. Prayers that Round 2 goes smoothly with no complications are needed. We are stronger when we fight together.

CHAPTER 9

JAN O'BRIEN

SISTER-IN-LAW, RESCUE ANGEL,
FORMER MAYO CLINIC NURSE, DEAR FRIEND

> *Jan, a retired triage nurse from Mayo Clinic and wife of Dan's brother Ron, left her home in Minnesota to stay with us for weeks on end to help care for me. Jan will help you **"find the joy in doing,"** which is something she demonstrated every single moment that we were together. To say she's my sister-in-law simply does not do our relationship justice. My sisters call her Angel Jan. So do I.*

I vividly remember the evening that we received an alarming telephone call from Dan, Maureen's husband. My husband (Dan's brother) Ron took the call. I listened from another room. I knew in my heart that the conversation was concerning. Dan was calling to share with us the diagnosis that Maureen had recently received. She was diagnosed with stage

4 diffuse large B-cell non-Hodgkin's lymphoma. Biopsies had confirmed the diagnosis, and Maureen had already had surgery to stabilize her femur because the cancer had done damage to the bone. Six rounds of chemotherapy treatments would begin when she healed from the surgery.

Thoughts immediately began fleeting through my mind. What should we do? What do we *need* to do? What can *I* do? How can we best help? Is Maureen going to survive? Terrifying, mind-racing questions.

I knew we must do something! Certainly, she needed to get treatment, and the sooner, the better. At the time, we offered to do whatever was needed, including traveling from Rochester, Minnesota, to Maureen and Dan's home. As a retired nurse, I offered to move in and help care for her. I was feeling helpless because of the distance between us, and many thoughts were bombarding my mind. I had trouble discerning what to do first. Dan let us know that he would keep us informed. He assured us that he would let us know if he needed anything. The conversation ended and we were in dismay. We just kept questioning how we could help.

Within the hour, Dan called back and asked if I could come soon and spend time with them to help care for Maureen. I immediately said yes. We packed and traveled the next day.

My stomach churned and my mind raced with thoughts of what we might find when we arrived. Would I know what to do? Would I be comfortable in their space? I had so many concerns, but I knew, deep down, that this was what I was being called to do. My Christian belief nudged me to step up to offer my love and care.

We were not prepared to see Maureen in such a weakened and vulnerable state. She was unable to walk on her own and needed physical support. She had to use a walker or wheelchair. More drastically, she appeared to have lost her spirit. We were used to seeing a woman full of life and energy, always willing to share herself with everyone around her. I felt so very scared and sad seeing how defeated Maureen was physically, mentally, emotionally, and spiritually.

My journey on this walk with Maureen and her family had begun. I started to make trips to the O'Brien home in Batavia, Illinois, spending a week or two at a time. As Maureen healed from her hip surgery and waited for chemo treatment to begin, Dan continued to work, and I stayed with Maureen during the day. It took me a while to be comfortable in her private space, but I decided to let go of my own fears and just be present to her. Maureen was open to all my love and care. She was fighting for her life!

As the days went by and as Maureen healed from her surgery, a plan of treatment for the lymphoma was in the making by her health care team. I watched her condition deteriorate. I kept thinking we needed to move forward, faster, sooner. The lymphoma seemed to be winning. I was terrified.

Maureen continued to decline. She was incredibly weak. We decided we needed to get her to the emergency room. Her family convened at the hospital. Maureen received fluids for dehydration, started to feel better, and wanted to go home. I just kept praying that they would keep her at the hospital and move forward with her treatment. They did.

After being admitted, several medical professionals joined forces to evaluate the situation. Multiple tests determined the decision to start chemo. I remember the primary oncologist walking into the room and saying to Dan, "Usually, we like to wait thirty days after a major surgery like your wife has had, but we need to move forward with the treatment now. We need to hit this very hard. We don't want to have to come back at it if we don't win in these first six rounds of chemo. If we have to come back at this a second time, it will be much more difficult to conquer."

As a nurse, I have always believed that one needs an advocate with them while in the hospital. I voiced that belief. Dan agreed, and we created a plan so that Maureen was not alone, day or night. Someone was always there to be a voice, an advocate, a sounding board, a cheerleader—whatever was necessary to help her. Family and friends took turns surrounding Maureen with love and positive support. It truly was beautiful to see!

> I HAVE ALWAYS BELIEVED THAT ONE NEEDS AN ADVOCATE WITH THEM WHILE IN THE HOSPITAL.

The treatments finally got underway. It was a grueling treatment plan, with each treatment requiring five continuous days and nights of chemo while hospitalized. It was very scary at times to see Maureen so vulnerable. I promised myself (and God) that I was ready to get through these difficult moments with her. I remember one night looking at the orange IV bag full of chemotherapy drugs and thinking, *How will her body ever tolerate this harsh treatment?*

I was not with her for all the treatments. When I was, I was proud to share my love and my nursing/caring skills. I certainly had moments of fear, often wondering if Maureen would survive. But I decided to put my full and complete trust in the health care team. The team proved to be amazing; they never faltered. Maureen was open to everything they had to offer, and her sense of hope prevailed. I believe in my heart that she survived because of love, hope, humor, and prayer, and I was deeply moved by Maureen's sense of gratitude toward it all.

Maureen's immediate family demonstrated unceasing love and were all "fully in." Even with the fear and unknowns of the situation, they never wavered. I realized the importance of belief in the ability of a person to survive such a difficult illness. Everyone must believe the treatment will work. Maureen's children were attentive, and they shared their time and love in so many ways. Having four children of my own, watching her kids broke my heart. But Maureen always seemed to light up when any of her grown children arrived at her home or the hospital. The respect and love that she had instilled in each of them throughout their lives were now paying dividends.

I REALIZED THE IMPORTANCE OF
BELIEF IN THE ABILITY OF A PERSON TO
SURVIVE SUCH A DIFFICULT ILLNESS.
EVERYONE MUST BELIEVE THE
TREATMENT WILL WORK.

Dan was the most extraordinary person to watch in this process. He was the rock through it all. Typically very quiet and unassuming, Dan readily stepped up and took charge. He wrapped his love around Maureen, and she hung on tight. Those are two other things that I'm convinced were a big factor in her ability to beat this disease: belief and love. Dan spent time at the hospital every day, even though he continued working. He kept their home going, kept the bills paid, kept the groceries coming, and kept the family organized and supported. I felt so well cared for and appreciated by Dan and the family. Dan has such a strong faith. I believe he leaned into and relied on his faith, and I believe his faith sustained him on this journey.

The O'Briens have a wonderful community of friends. It was amazing how that community circled around the family in their desperate need. They were respectful of the family's privacy, but when called upon, they mobilized. Maureen loves the outdoors and particularly her backyard. It has always been her oasis. Because Maureen was not able, a group of about twenty-five people—the Garden Angels—joined together in the spring to bring beauty to the backyard of Maureen's home. I witnessed the absolute loving spirit of these angels, who gave with no expectation of anything in return. This was simply their gift of love, a way for them to be present. Other people sent food, cards, gift cards, gifts to share, and a whole lot of prayers. The outpouring of friendship and love proved to me just how important it is to be present in some way—any way. It is healing for all of us to share our love and feelings in the difficult times in people's lives. I witnessed firsthand the positive effect it has on a person who is struggling and their family.

THE OUTPOURING OF FRIENDSHIP AND LOVE
PROVED TO ME JUST HOW IMPORTANT IT IS
TO BE PRESENT IN SOME WAY—ANY WAY.

While I was not present for every day of this journey, I am grateful that I allowed myself to be part of it as I could. It was difficult facing my own feelings, and I certainly felt sad each time I had to leave her. We developed such a strong bond, but even when I had to leave, I always knew she was in the loving care of many who loved her. Maureen and I shared sadness, fear, love, and a lot of laughter, as well as middle-of-the-night chocolate peanut butter ice cream . . . all of which provided strength for both of us.

I believe Maureen continues to be a survivor because of her positive outlook on life, her faith, her loving husband, and the all-encompassing love of her children, extended family, and community of friends. My role was to support her and to hold her in love on this journey. Watching her fight for her life led all of us to the end zone. This experience has made me a better person and has helped me to appreciate every day as a blessing. I certainly was honored to be included with all the other angels who helped Maureen on this journey.

ILLUMINATIONS

If you are reading this and in a similar circumstance, I hope you will take this away from my story: Be present, stay in the moment, find joy. Believe. Give your love in any way that you can. Don't ask what you can do. Just do. You can make such a big difference . . . even in, and sometimes *especially in*, the smallest of things that you do. When you make the choice to *show up* in someone else's life, most particularly when they are in need, good things happen.

Blessings to you on your journey as part of a community of care.

ROUND 2 STARTS—PROTOCOL GOING WELL

Journal Entry by Britta McKenna

April 13, 2016

Round 2 started April 11. We're now halfway through Round 2, and things are going much better this round. Maureen is tolerating the chemo well and was able to do a lap around the floor today with her walker and Dan at her side. Sister-in-law, Jan and Dan have been rotating companionship with Mo the past three days with sister Karen coming tomorrow afternoon for a sleepover. Your prayers are working their magic this round and the fact that her doctor didn't take her "down" so far with the meds. Mo's pneumonia is still lingering a bit, being stubborn to leave her lungs so she still battles a cough, but nothing compared to a couple weeks ago. If things continue on this path, Mo will finish Round 2 on Friday and will be headed for home. Pray on!

ROUND 2 IS IN THE BOOKS!

Journal Entry by Britta McKenna
April 16, 2016

Maureen finished Round 2 strong last night and is home enjoying the gorgeous spring day on her back deck. She is thankful for the small things and happy to be home. Many thanks to all who have delivered food to the family. It continues to be a blessing.

CHAPTER 10

LINDA MCINTYRE

SISTER-IN-LAW, FRIEND

> *Linda, Dan's sister, is a giver. She is always willing to help and first in line when anyone has a need. She writes about **"lending a helping hand,"** which is something that she does naturally. There is always something you can do, some way to help. Linda will help you find your way.*

I'm not exactly sure who delivered the news, but I remember clearly how I felt. I was in complete disbelief. Of all the people I knew, I never thought Maureen would get a cancer diagnosis. I know cancer is not discretionary, but there are just some people who seem bigger or tougher than a diagnosis like this. Cancer wouldn't dare!

Next came grief, real sadness, and an overwhelming feeling of helplessness. I wondered how my brother Dan would handle all of this. I had just completed years of being the caregiver for my own husband. I knew Dan would be thrust into something overwhelming. He would need to concentrate his full focus on three things: his wife, his kids, and the doctors. He would have to listen to the doctors. Listen and comprehend. Make decisions that would be terrifying. *Oh my God*, this *is* happening.

The barrage of phone calls began: one from our brother Ron and then from his wife Jan. Each was more troubling than the last. My head was spinning. Again, such a feeling of helplessness. All I could do was pray. Even as I write this almost five years later, the memory of getting that news causes so many tears.

SUCH A FEELING OF HELPLESSNESS. ALL I COULD DO WAS PRAY.

"I need to go." I remember thinking that and saying those words out loud to an empty room. It was like I expected the walls to affirm my decision and encourage me. Then I wondered if that was really the best plan. Would I simply be in the way? Maybe going right now is not the answer. I am not needed now. Wait. Just wait. And pray. Pray. Pray.

Help comes in waves. Food for the family, housekeeping, cards. All these things are necessary and of great help. Jan decided that she would go and stay with the family. Perhaps they could use her nursing skills, and she could be a help to the kids, who, even though they were adults, were traumatized at the news.

A month went by, and aggressive chemo started. In that same month, the flu and pneumonia set in. How would she survive this? How does a body endure so much? Two months passed; reports were mixed. Chemo is so rough. Three months.

Finally, my brother asked me to come. The request was that I go from Minnesota to Illinois to stay with the family for two weeks so that sister-in-law Jan could go home and get a break. I was more than ready yet anxious about what I might find. When I arrived, I found Maureen to be frail and weak. She had lost forty pounds, yet the spark had come back into her eyes.

In the two weeks that I was at the house, I celebrated my birthday. With everything that Maureen was going through, she still found a way to make that day special for me. A teddy bear, offering *me* comfort, showed up in my room. Her sisters came, and one more time, Maureen had to make her way to the hospital for a week's stay and a round of chemo.

The weather was beginning to change, and I would sometimes catch Maureen just staring out the window. I knew she longed to get out in her yard. But that wasn't possible. She walked with a walker and was not able to be upright for long periods of time. A sadness was starting to take over—so a call went out on the CaringBridge Site for Garden Angels.

And the angels responded. Flats of flowers began to show up on the front porch. On the Saturday of Memorial Day weekend, twenty-five angels came to convert Maureen's backyard to the oasis she loved. You do not realize how important the small things like planting flowers—adding color, adding life—mean to someone who is locked in the house. Those angels transformed what looked dull, tired, and gray into bursts of color and life. The interesting thing is, the "giving" from the angels was as awe-inspiring for them as it was for Maureen. What seemed like such a small gesture created life, community, goodness, laughter, companionship, and a sense of well-being.

YOU DO NOT REALIZE HOW IMPORTANT
THE SMALL THINGS MEAN TO SOMEONE
WHO IS LOCKED IN THE HOUSE.

I came home feeling relieved. The family was coping, and I believed *they* would be OK. There were still a couple of rounds of chemo ahead, but somehow, I knew in my heart, *she* would be OK.

On July 20, when I received the call that Maureen was in remission, that the cancer was really gone, tears flowed again! Tears of such joy. The future was still going to be full of doctor's appointments, blood tests, and scans, but I knew—*we knew*—she had done it. She had beaten the opponent. Just like I thought in the beginning: cancer never had a chance.

And the prayers continue . . .

ILLUMINATIONS

It's important to lend a helping hand wherever you can. (When in doubt, pray for guidance!) The gift of bringing joy to a loved one suffering a critical illness can be just what's needed to boost morale and encourage hope.

THREE REASONS TO GIVE THANKS

Journal Entry by Britta McKenna

April 20, 2016

Checking in today with Mo and family gave me pause for thanks. First, I was greeted by a cleaned up yard, compliments of an angel who sent a landscaping company. Second, Mo told me her blood counts are in the normal range and she hasn't had to go to the cancer center for an infusion since Monday. Third, Dan's sister, Linda showed me the beautiful quilt (pictured) that she just finished.

Mo has a lingering cough and tires easily and thankfully that is it for the not so nice report. Loads to be thankful for, including a nice spring rain tonight and warm weather on the way again this weekend.

PART

3

BUSINESS ASSOCIATES

AS POINTS OF LIGHT

The impact of a cancer diagnosis goes so far beyond immediate and extended family. Work colleagues and business associates are often aware of the diagnosis, but they often feel helpless and find it difficult to know what to do.

We have been so blessed in the extension of love beyond our family circle. Dan's boss, Ed Curtis, focused more on how to stand *with* and *for* Dan than on work. Jill Blanchard, one of my board members, and Rita Johnson, my former partner, share the impact (and loss) of a business leader and partner and their willingness to step up in the interim.

CHAPTER 11

ED CURTIS

DAN'S BOSS

If you look up the word "boss" in the dictionary, you'll find a picture of Ed Curtis. Correction: you'd have to look up the words "great boss"!

Ed was such a pillar of strength for Dan throughout my diagnosis and treatment. While I was unaware at the time of all that Ed did, I was acutely aware of the amount of time Dan was able to spend with me. I desperately needed that time with him. As Ed shares, his belief of **"family first, work follows"** *is writing I wish every boss would read and internalize. It makes all the difference.*

I started working with Maureen's husband, Dan, in 2008 in a facility that manufactures paperboard. As Dan and I began our new working relationship, it became apparent to both of us that we operated very differently. I was new in this industry, but I normally try to learn fast and have a habit of making decisions quickly: ready, shoot, aim. Dan had already been at our location for several years. He was very good in his role. *Very* detailed. One of our early work discussions involved finding a better balance for our relationship between having *enough* information to make the best decision versus having *all* of the information. This discussion laid the groundwork for many conversations as our relationship grew.

It soon became clear that Dan is a man of great wisdom. He is very thoughtful in his words and actions. He thinks . . . and thinks . . . and thinks about his decisions and conversations before ever acting. I have a lot of room to grow in this area. One of the quotes hanging in Dan's office is from the book of James in the Bible: "Be quick to listen, slow to speak, slow to anger." Dan lived this. I did not. I had much to learn from Dan as a leader. Dan is a quiet, influential, informal leader.

Our regular conversation topics grew from just work, to our families, our roles as fathers, sons, husbands, our dreams, and our faith. Dan and I have some commonalities, and we have many differences. However, we both listened and learned from each other. As a father of four and husband to a dynamic leader like Maureen, Dan had much wisdom to share in our friendship. He always listened intently to my views, opinions, and thoughts.

As our talks grew more into our faith and beliefs, we realized we are very aligned, and we were intrigued by each other's walk and challenges. It was clear that the God and Savior we both put our faith in is the same one for a Catholic from Minnesota as for a Baptist from Tennessee. God's love and grace is unifying. Our friendship had grown to include regular conversations and even prayers together about our life's struggles and opportunities.

Fast-forward to the amazingly difficult conversation when Dan told me that his beautiful bride ("Da Bride," as he often refers to Maureen) was having some medical issues. At first, it was a concern about Mo's shoulder, then probable surgery, to something isn't right, to full-blown horrible news: Maureen has a very aggressive cancer. Today, five years later, the exact details of our conversation are a blur. What I do remember is that we prayed together immediately, and then I told him to go home. Work is work. We can and will figure it out, but his one and only priority at that moment should be Maureen.

That was the first of many times I repeated this to Dan. Not because Dan ever doubted where he should be, but because Dan's lifelong work ethic told him he should not "cheat" work. These are my words, not his. Dan knew where he needed to be and was always there. Our team at work was amazing. They all pulled together and communicated the same message: being with Maureen and supporting her in every way was now Dan's job. I don't recall talking to Dan about any work schedule details early in Maureen's treatment. That was not the time. Dan just needed to know it was not just OK for him to be with Maureen, but it was our expectation.

I had the privilege of praying with Dan many times during these days. We also prayed for Maureen at my church and in our small prayer group. In one of our small group meetings,

not too long after Maureen's diagnosis, I had just shared an update and asked for prayer for my coworker's wife when another
group member mentioned they had just been told by a friend
of a friend to pray for this incredible lady in Batavia who has
cancer . . . Maureen.

I cannot say how long, how hard, or how many times
Maureen was prayed for by me and by the hundreds if not
thousands of other people that she, Dan, and their family have
touched, but I know that God knew there were many people
on His earth who loved and cared for her and wanted—no,
expected—her to be healed.

We do not understand God's ways. We don't know why certain
things occur when others don't. What I do know is that God is
still in the miracle business. God's promises are clear; our faith
ignites God's power. Maureen is living proof of faith in action,
both from God and from His people. It is my privilege to play
a small part in supporting Dan and being part of the community of care. It was not an individual effort but a team effort. I
was driven by my love for Dan and God.

Too often, I hear the call to be His hands and feet but get
too busy or lost in the noise to act. This was an easy action.
I wanted to help Dan focus on caring for his beautiful bride
and family. Supporting Dan in every possible way to allow him
to be strong for those who needed it most allowed him to be
transparent and honest with me. Dan had been investing in me
for years, trying to teach me to listen first. Now was my time to
listen and support him. Nothing I did was in my own wisdom

or strength. I was simply being obedient to our great Savior, Jesus, day by day.

Getting to tell our church family and small group of Maureen's progress and recovery was special. It was like water to someone thirsty. Later, getting to hear Maureen tell her story firsthand to large groups and see how it impacted everyone was the reward of a miracle fulfilled.

I still have a long way to grow. I still talk too much, act too fast, don't listen well. But when I slow down, trust God for today, and respond to His call to act as His hands and feet, I avail glory to God. Too many times we hear "religion" has no place at work. I don't look at it that way. My faith should drive the whole person I am all the time, whether I'm at home, work, school, or church. I don't ever want to be thought of as a "religious person"; I want to be consistent in my faith and have faith's actions show up in everything I do. Faith should impact my behavior, conversations, and actions everywhere. Especially at work. It's better. Our ability to be our whole person allows us to care for others, show empathy, and build relationships.

> I WANT TO BE CONSISTENT IN MY FAITH AND HAVE FAITH'S ACTIONS SHOW UP IN EVERYTHING I DO. FAITH SHOULD IMPACT MY BEHAVIOR, CONVERSATIONS, AND ACTIONS EVERYWHERE.

Being Dan's friend and walking beside him is my privilege. Being part of his community of care, Maureen's community, was my honor.

ILLUMINATIONS

There is a work balance to strike when it comes to doing the right things from an HR perspective (privacy, FMLA, not crossing certain lines), but caring practically and with love for a friend and coworker is always the right thing to do.

Take care of the employee first, worry about the paperwork and process later, and simply reassure them that they don't have to worry about the work. Taking care of their loved one is their *only* priority. Work challenges have many solutions, but being present for their family must be their immediate and only concern.

10 ROUND 3, DELAYED START

Journal Entry by Britta McKenna
April 25, 2016

Today was to be the first day of Round 3 chemo. Unfortunately Mo's blood counts were too low to start chemo today. The day was spent at the hospital with waiting, resting, some testing and lots of peanut M&M's. Sister Karen was there to bring smiles and encouragement and despite a fire alarm at the hospital, I managed a short visit to get information for this update after being contained in the center area of the hospital when fire doors were automatically closed. Alas, tomorrow is another day and hopefully, just a delay to the first day of Round 3. We call on our prayer warriors to carry us through again. You all are incredible—keep the encouragement coming!

CHAPTER 12

JILL BLANCHARD

EXECUTIVE, ADVISORY BOARD MEMBER OF GLOBAL
WOMEN'S LEADERSHIP FORUM; CLIENT

> *Jill was one of the few board members with whom I shared my health journey. She is more than a board member; she is a dear friend. Jill is honest, transparent, and kind, and she will help you recognize the importance of **"being there"** in any way that you are able when someone is in crisis.*

She was sick with worry and had a call to arms for prayer. What started out as an unsolvable shoulder issue turned into—after several misdiagnoses—a test for something more serious. I got the text. Non-Hodgkin's lymphoma. OK . . . that's not so bad, right? I immediately consulted the expert: Google. I don't recall exactly what I read, but I remember learning it was highly treatable and had a high survival rate. OK. This is good . . . it could be worse. She's going to be OK! I launched my response.

I recognized the diagnosis and the fact that it sounded—well, I didn't use these words—like one of the better kinds of cancer if you were going to get cancer.

It's hard to write this. If I only knew. If I only knew what she would have to go through over the next year plus to come out the other side. If I only knew the seriousness of the diagnosis and that "coming out the other side" was far from guaranteed—and that "the other side" was this elusive place to which she is only granted interim access. If I only knew how this would change her and her family's lives forever. If I only knew how many times she would have to wait for test results that may or may not grant her a few months of less worry.

I've always prided myself on recognizing the difference between sympathy and empathy. It's one thing to not know how someone else feels when they suffer a loss. It's altogether another thing to not know how someone else feels when they're scared for their life. Their actual life. Now I have a view from the outside of what this looks like. But when I first got the text . . . well, I thought she got the good kind of cancer diagnosis.

IT'S ONE THING TO NOT KNOW HOW SOMEONE ELSE FEELS WHEN THEY SUFFER A LOSS. IT'S ALTOGETHER ANOTHER THING TO NOT KNOW HOW SOMEONE ELSE FEELS WHEN THEY'RE SCARED FOR THEIR LIFE.

Everyone knows cancer treatments can range from not so bad to unthinkable. Short of experiencing this with a loved one, the ramifications of a cancer diagnosis are incomprehensible. My life has been blessed in so many ways, one of which is the fact that I've never had this experience.

Each of her treatment rounds required a one-week hospital stay. After a few rounds (yes, I waited before visiting—ugh), it seemed that she could have visitors while undergoing treatment. I launched another of my texts. Was it just that I'm a texter? Or was I afraid to call? I don't know, but I soon received the cheerful response so reminiscent of her: "Yes, come by any time!" Oh boy. What. Took. Me. So. Long? I wanted to create a good day for her.

A friend of mine once had an extended hospital stay while recovering from a car accident. We used to have spa days where we did facials, painted our toes—just regular girl stuff to help pass the time and momentarily forget about the tubes and monitors and pain. I pulled together my spa gift bag and headed out to see Maureen.

Two things struck me when I walked into her room. The first I'll never forget. She had lost all her hair and had a scarf on her head with her traditional lip color, and she was beautiful. Like she always was. I don't think she even looked different without her hair. Her eyes and her smile are what defines her, and she was still herself. It warmed me and immediately put me at ease.

GOD BLESS COMPANIES AND BOSSES WHO FIND A WAY—NO MATTER THE COST—TO GRANT PEOPLE THIS IN THEIR TIME OF NEED.

131

The second was her husband, sitting dutifully by her side. I thought to myself, *Of course he's there,* but I also thought, *How? It's the middle of the week! Is his job giving him this time off? God bless companies and bosses who find a way—no matter the cost—to grant people this in their time of need.*

What I learned over the next few hours stunned me. Cancer treatment is like the house that Jack built. This affects that, that affects this over here, this over here affects that one, and so on and so on. We weren't going to do a spa day. She was sick. And while her cancer treatment was working to cure her, it was attacking her at the same time. She wasn't dodging bullets. She was taking on bullets to save her life.

A few weeks later, her friends rounded up a gardening task force. They cleaned up her yard and planted flowers galore. I didn't join. I couldn't make it. Ugh. For all the times we say and think, "If there's anything I can do . . ." In retrospect, the gardening task force was brilliant. She didn't have to ask (she would never), yet this is something she enjoyed every day. She loves color and life, and blooming potted flowers enveloping her backyard is the perfect personification of how she lives and projects life. I don't remember what I was doing in lieu of this, but I'll always remember that whatever it was, I was in the wrong place.

ILLUMINATIONS

I'd like to think I've learned something from this and can now be a better person, even without empathy, to a loved one suffering. They need us. Not us on their good day. Not us when it's convenient. Not us asking them what we can do.

The most valuable thing we can do is show up. Be. Be an ear, a smile, a shoulder, some light. It was less important for me to tell her what I thought her diagnosis meant and more important to just be there. Say you'll be there, and be there. It was less important for me to make a great treatment day for her. It was more important to be there. And nothing—literally nothing—can be a higher priority than bringing color and life to help someone confined to the gray and suffering hold on to life.

DELAY OF GAME PLAN

Journal Entry by Britta McKenna

April 26, 2016

Round 3 has not gone as planned. Today Maureen was sent home from the hospital and unable to start chemo due to low blood counts. She is susceptible to infection so the family asks that we keep visitors at bay this week. Mo will rest up and try again next week. Please send crazy cards, funny jokes and other interesting ways to pass for her to pass the time. If you feel like cooking, sign up here to drop off a meal for the family.

THE POWERFUL MEDICINE OF FAMILY

Journal Entry by Britta McKenna

April 30, 2016

Mo is arming herself for Round 3 with the best kind of medicine: the power of family. Dan's sister Linda is headed home while Nurse Jan (sister-in-law) is coming in to stay tomorrow. Sister Patricia and hubby Terry are here for the weekend and the house is full of love and support. Though it was a long, disappointing week of waiting, counts went WAY up by Friday, so keep those prayers coming that she'll be ready for Monday to get going on Round 3. #LoveAlwaysWins

ROUND 3 UNDERWAY

Journal Entry by Britta McKenna

May 2, 2016

Today at 3:00 p.m. Round 3 of chemo began at Northwestern. Maureen is tolerating the protocol so far; the doctor is taking her back to the same chemo cocktail as Round 1, so extra prayers are needed to lift her up through the week. Mo is stocked up with peanut M&M's with the fam on hand. #lovealwayswins

JUST ONE MORE NIGHT

Journal Entry by Britta McKenna

May 5, 2016

We had a good day yesterday AND a good night. Mo woke up this morning with the thought of "just one more night" (at the hospital). A very nice thought indeed as she passed the halfway mark for chemo yesterday.

I wanted to share with all you the beautiful picture entitled, "Woman Weaving Love in the World," given to Mo by her kids last weekend. The kids said it is Mo in the picture, but I already knew that. What a wonderful reminder and way to start our day as we remember why we are "here" and what is truly important in life. #lovealwayswins

MOTHER'S DAY AT HOME

Journal Entry by Britta McKenna

May 8, 2016

Maureen, Dan and the four kids were all home today to enjoy a beautiful Mother's Day together. Oh, and Riley was home visiting all weekend and we can't forget about Jan either. There were brats grilled out, a competitive sibling game of bags on the deck and a long afternoon nap for Mo. So, all in all, the house was pretty "normal." Though Mo has battled waves of nausea since coming home Friday night, it is always good to be home.

CHAPTER 13

RITA JOHNSON

FRIEND, FORMER BUSINESS PARTNER

> *Rita had the undesirable position of being the closest person to me in the business when I was diagnosed. She had just retired—or thought she had—when she was immediately thrust back into leading a work environment that she believed she'd left behind.*
>
> *Rita will help you understand the importance of **"minimizing stress factors"** whenever and however you can for the person who has been diagnosed.*

I was sitting in my home office in Arizona when Nicole, my daughter-in-law—who was Maureen's executive assistant—called to tell me that Mo had cancer. I had retired from my position with the Global Women's Leadership Forum several months before, and I was not expecting a call about work, much less about Mo.

I was shocked. I said a quick prayer and asked for more details. Then I started trying to understand what was needed from me at that point. What did Maureen need me to do? What were the outstanding commitments that had been made? What questions did Nicole have that I could help answer? I understood the role I could play for the company, and I was more than willing to contribute to the business I had helped to build.

Over the course of the next few days, several people called to talk to me about the business: Maureen's sister Karen, whom I knew from our work, and Britta McKenna, the best friend anyone could ever think to have. I told both Karen and Britta that I *could not* take Maureen's place in the business and that I did not want to. I believe that this message hurt both Maureen and me in a way that I had not intended or expected.

Her diagnosis was coming near the fifth anniversary of my mother's death from cancer, a journey that was so painful and pain-filled that the thought of it was often paralyzing for me. In hindsight and reflection, I have come to realize that my reactions to Maureen's personal journey were colored by the pain, regret, and anger I still felt about my mother's journey through cancer.

I have known fifteen people with cancer. Six of those souls are no longer with us. The good news is that this puts odds on the plus side. And there are two people that I *never* believed would die from cancer: my husband and Maureen O'Brien. I just simply refused to entertain the thought.

Certainly, when my husband was first diagnosed, I agonized through the "normal" responses—this cannot be true, we have a young son, what are the treatment options, what do we do next, what would I do without him—and then, after a few brief bouts of anxiety, I realized *he needed me to believe* in his full recovery. Once I committed to that decision, I never looked back. I constantly affirmed only positive thoughts that he would be healthy again, and he is. Cancer-free for twenty years!

> WE DETERMINE THE COURSE OF OUR LIVES THROUGH THE POWER OF OUR THOUGHTS, WHETHER CONSCIOUS OR UNCONSCIOUS.

I am a firm believer in the power of co-creation. We determine the course of our lives through the power of our thoughts, whether conscious or unconscious, and so I try every day to stay on the positive side. With Mo, after having a few harrowing conversations and learning more about her cancer, I affirmed the positive and again stopped entertaining any other thoughts.

Whenever I thought of Maureen, I said, "Thank you, God, for Mo's perfect healing," and I believed that her perfect healing was that she would survive. I know that "perfect healing" does not always mean life. Sometimes it means moving on to the next place. That has been my experience with six different people, including my own mother.

> "PERFECT HEALING" DOES NOT ALWAYS MEAN LIFE. SOMETIMES IT MEANS MOVING ON TO THE NEXT PLACE.

I have honestly never thought much about my own mortality when hearing about someone else's diagnosis. I don't know why. I just don't ever remember thinking about it. I was at my mother's side when she died, and even then, my *own* mortality never entered the story for me. Perhaps it's because I'm not afraid of death. I *am* afraid of having regrets after someone else passes: regrets that I didn't spend time with them as I should have . . . could have . . . or that I didn't know *how* to spend time with them. But dying does not frighten me.

I understood that Maureen's journey would be long and arduous, and I knew that she had an amazing support system of both family and friends. I had watched her cultivate those relationships over a six-year period of working closely with her. I knew she would never be alone. I also knew *that* was where her strength would come from.

Maureen creates an intention for her day, every day. She begins her day with spiritual reading and writing and then finishes with an intention. And there would be no other intention regarding this diagnosis than *life*. Because I knew that about her, until and unless I heard something dire and understood that there were no other medical options for her, I believed she would live. I moved forward with that as *my* intention.

Because I lived in Southern Arizona—almost to Mexico—I was not part of the local community of angels who supported Maureen and the O'Brien clan. Those who can physically care for and be present with someone undergoing cancer treatment have a completely different view of the patient and their needs.

With that distance, I focused on what I *could* contribute, knowing it was fulfilling the business's commitments that had been made to members and clients. I could do that for Maureen in her absence. I knew in my heart that while it was not the same as sitting with Maureen during chemo or just being with her, it was also critically important for her peace of mind to know that someone who had helped build the business and who understood the work was doing what needed to be done to ensure that the name and the brand of the business remained strong. It felt like the only real gift I could bring.

In hindsight, I realized that I had taken at face value, without confirmation, a message I had read on Maureen's CaringBridge site from Dan, her amazing, loving spouse. He had posted early on that visitors were not really welcomed at the hospital . . . something that made perfect sense to me in terms of weakened immune systems and harsh physical responses to chemo and radiation. And so I stayed away, thinking that this was the best course of action. I didn't reach out to Maureen personally because I understood from her brief writings that chemo brain was happening—something I was intimately familiar with, as it had slowly robbed my mother of her ability to stay present and focused. That decision, misguided but sincere, kept me out of the community. A regret.

> I STAYED AWAY, THINKING THAT THIS
> WAS THE BEST COURSE OF ACTION. THAT
> MISGUIDED DECISION KEPT ME OUT OF
> THE COMMUNITY. A REGRET.

I believe it is impossible to go through someone's cancer treatment without thinking about others we know/knew and their outcomes. Those memories can unconsciously color our perspectives and our reactions to the current reality. Becoming aware of our own relationship with cancer, death, and mortality and our ability to puzzle through our emotions can help us discern the best response to what is in front of us.

ILLUMINATIONS

This would be my advice to others. First, be gentle with yourself as you process and move through this journey and time. It is hard work, and it can bring up so many layers of memories and past messages that we can become confused between what is currently going on and what happened in the past. Choosing responses that seem best in the moment can cause pain and regret later. Give yourself permission to step back from the need to make immediate decisions so that you have some distance and time in which to make a more informed and discerning decision.

Second, our affection, our consideration, and our being available is *always* welcomed . . . even if it doesn't feel like it or look like it in the moment. Whatever you can give, contribute. The effort is often all that is needed. Holding a hand, bringing a warm blanket, or just sitting and watching the world go by is always enough, especially when it comes from a place of love, care, and affection.

I remember being with my mother eighteen months before she died, sitting in the sunshine on my patio . . . just sitting and listening to the birds . . . not talking . . . and suddenly she said, "It's so nice to just sit and be quiet." I understood that was all she wanted from me in that moment . . . and it was enough.

THE LONG WAIT

Journal Entry by Britta McKenna
May 12, 2016

Mo has been a bit restless at home this week. Up and down with nausea and feeling tired, but mostly stuck in the tired of waiting phase. As she has felt ok this round, her angst in waiting includes Round 4 chemo and getting her PET scan Tuesday. Need all your powerful prayers for a positive test tomorrow.

While we are waiting, please hold the date of Saturday, May 28 when all you angels are invited to participate in "Flowers for Mo." We all know Mo loves to be outside in the summer and as she is the flower planter, she'll need our help to get ready for the season. I am looking for volunteers to drop off flowers and help planting. I'll post more details about types of flowers and quantities after I get back from Switzerland. Yes, this scribe is in Switzerland with my better half for the next 9 days. While we are away, I will not post, but you may hear from Dan or Maureen if they have updates.

Signing off for a bit so I can find chocolate, fondue, a yodeling lesson, Heidi, Swiss cheese, a new watch, family Von Trapp or Swiss Family Robinson.

PART

4

FRIENDS

AS POINTS OF LIGHT

It is still astounding to me how many friends and neighbors desired to participate in our community of care. But I'm not sure that's unusual. Most people want to help. It's just that they often don't know what to do.

You will learn a great deal from our friends and neighbors and the extension of love that they provided the O'Brien family. I've always known that love heals. Never has this been truer than in my journey with lymphoma.

CHAPTER 14

BRITTA W. MCKENNA

INCREDIBLE FRIEND, ORGANIZER OF THE PLAYBOOK

If you look up the word "shero" in the dictionary, there you'll find Britta. Quarterback, Project Manager, Gatekeeper, Twister Spinner, Shero . . . whatever you call her, she and her husband Steve held the playbook for organizing and executing support for the team beyond the O'Brien/Vernal family.

*It has become so very clear that everyone facing a cancer journey needs a Britta in their lives. Britta has offered a playbook. She'll share in a step-by-step fashion how to **"execute the plays."** (This chapter could be a book in and of itself!) I hope you'll utilize it as such. And I hope you, too, have a friend like Britta in your life.*

I don't remember exactly when, where, or how I found out about Mo's illness. That part is but a blur for me. Shock does that to the body. Maybe it is reality's way of providing a personal protective coating for really bad news. The exact details are not of great significance to me anymore, but I do realize they are important for families of those diagnosed with a life-threatening illness.

The chaos of the early stage of any serious diagnosis finds family and friends searching for the "why" and "how" as the first stage of grief invades: denial. For the patient and their family, the waiting game begins with getting in to see a doctor (or the next doctor), enduring the barrage of tests and interpreting results, and getting a treatment plan together. It all adds up to a whirlwind of stress and anxiety. For me, the early stages of Mo's diagnosis felt like I was in the middle of a game of Twister with her family members, waiting for my turn to spin.

Before I spin, let's back up a bit. My side of Mo's story rewinds to sometime in the 1990s when a friendship developed as our paths started crossing at church, at our kids' school, and in the community. I'm not sure if I met Maureen or "Uh Oh," her clown persona, first—they are both memorable. (Yes, she really *is* a professional clown: she graduated from clown college in addition to her teaching degree.) Our lives have been interwoven for decades. She is one person I have depended on during my life trials to be there for me when I needed it most. Once I heard "stage 4 lymphoma," it was unquestionably my turn to be there for her.

In the fall of 2016, Mo had been complaining on and off about her shoulder. "Dr. Mo" self-diagnosed her pain as a rotator cuff tear without seeing an orthopedic doctor. I remember encouraging her to see a real doctor, but her response was classic: "I don't have time to have rotator cuff surgery."

If only that had been it.

After the holidays, it became increasingly evident that something was wrong; her physical therapy wasn't working, and her therapist encouraged her to go to the orthopedic doctor. Soon, the story began to unfold. Immediate care was needed. And quickly. The diagnosis developed rapidly at that point. Time was the enemy, and every day without treatment was another twenty-four hours that would allow cancer to invade. By the time I was in the loop, Mo had been through a battery of tests, and she was having surgery to put a rod next to her femur to stabilize it before it fractured from the cancer now ravaging her body.

What? It was just supposed to be rotator cuff surgery. Yes, an "inconvenience," but I'd bring over some popcorn from our local popcorn stand, we'd watch a few sappy movies and chat it up, and she'd be back to her "normal" self after a few weeks of physical therapy.

Nope.

Everything was happening so quickly, yet it seemed like I was watching the family play Twister in slow motion from the edge of the mat. Worry that I shouldn't intrude soon was overshadowed by my desire to grab the spinner. Pacing, I thought, *What would Mo do?* And the answer was simple—just show up. Hopping in my car, I wondered what I was doing, but I felt compelled to be there for her, wherever "there" was at the time.

EVERYTHING WAS HAPPENING SO QUICKLY, YET IT SEEMED LIKE I WAS WATCHING THE FAMILY PLAY TWISTER IN SLOW MOTION FROM THE EDGE OF THE MAT. WORRY THAT I SHOULDN'T INTRUDE SOON WAS OVERSHADOWED BY MY DESIRE TO GRAB THE SPINNER.

Arriving at the hospital post–femur stabilization surgery, I lurked in the hallway peering in, not sure if I should enter her room or wait outside. I hadn't been invited. It's hard being just outside the family circle and not in the loop. I selfishly wanted to know firsthand. My closest friend, who was "fine" last month, was now recovering from surgery, diagnosed with stage 4 non-Hodgkin's lymphoma. Unsure what to do next, I just wanted to be there for the family while things were unsettled and treatment options were still being discerned.

I remember talking with members of the family in the hallway while she slept. I did not go into the room. Maybe it was my way of keeping reality at bay. Quickly, the gravity of her diagnosis and her fight ahead was all too real. I immediately recognized this unwelcome wave of grief and sorrow as it rippled through me. Briefly, my mind revisited the battle my sister-in-law Nancy had with stage 4 lung cancer ten years prior and my stepmom Ruta's recent ALS journey. This devastating feeling was all too familiar. I had way too much practice in this arena, and the reality of that made me sick. Deep breath . . . because both Nancy and Ruta didn't survive. *But this is Mo,* I thought. And if anyone can defy the odds and beat this thing, it is Maureen Vernal-O'Brien.

I allowed myself the pause to be sad, to mourn the loss of normal for Mo, and to listen to the family and hear what they needed. It's what I do. Start with empathy by listening, gather facts, and help chart a course forward. It wasn't long before the pain of realization was behind me and I had begun weaving together a plan. I grabbed the Twister spinner and began calling out directions. That plan started with offering the family the specific help they needed to get organized and communicate with Mo's community who were eager for news.

I knew instinctively that the O'Brien family needed help, because this was not my first trip down Stage 4 Lane. Giving my role in Mo's care a title seems unnecessary since I just did what needed to be done. However, recently, I participated in "COVID TV Mass" from Holy Name Cathedral in Chicago with Cardinal Cupich on the third Sunday of Advent. During the Cardinal's homily, he told a story referencing a word I was unfamiliar with: *shosben*. In the Jewish culture during the time of Christ, the best man was called the "friend of the bridegroom" and oversaw everything. The shosben was the number one guard and liaison between the bride and bridegroom before the wedding happened. John the Baptist referred to himself in this way in relation to Jesus. The Greeks called the person with this role the *paranymph*, which can also refer to a "ceremonial assistant and/or coach in a ceremony." While close, even that word was not quite right, so I kept searching.

People need tangible ways to participate, invitations to something concrete they can and want to do. Part of my role in Mo's care was bringing people together and helping them see how they are connected to her. My role was providing concrete ways for people who cared for Mo to contribute to her care.

Dan has referred to me as a "project manager," although that title seems a bit sterile for this role. Staying in the Twister game metaphor, "spinner" I think accurately describes the position. Better yet is the point guard position in basketball; quarterback (QB) in football seems a better fit to imagine the role. As a former athlete, I most resonate with positions of team leadership: scanning the field or court, assessing the competitions and adjusting during the game, executing plays and passing the ball to team members to execute. Yes, QB seems the most fitting analogy, as it takes an entire team effort to win the game. Though the title is not important, the work certainly is.

> PEOPLE NEED TANGIBLE WAYS
> TO PARTICIPATE, INVITATIONS TO
> SOMETHING CONCRETE THEY CAN
> AND WANT TO DO.

The O'Briens didn't know they needed a QB, because this was their first time dealing with a life-threatening illness, but from my own past experiences, I knew where we needed to go. As a graduate of the Stage 4 School of Hard Knocks, I had a playbook. So, rather than leaving the O'Briens in their game of Twister, I grabbed the spinner, dusted off my playbook, and went to work.

The biggest issue at hand was the need for someone to handle initial communications outside the family. As Maureen is a "big" personality (remember, she is a professional clown, speaker, and business owner), I knew dozens of people would want to participate in her circle of care. I also knew from past personal experience that Dan's phone would soon be a hotspot for questions from well-meaning people if a channel was not set up quickly. It made sense for me to step in: someone close yet outside the immediate family circle. Someone who could mentally step back from the familial emotions and stress outside the home and get to work. I just jumped in blindly. I didn't ask; I simply offered my assistance in a matter-of-fact way to Dan.

Now, if you don't know Dan, he's a quiet, private, keep-to-himself guy, and that is perfect for Mo's life partner, but maybe not for dealing with her "bigness." Let me explain. Mo is not like Dan. In fact, if you looked up the antonym for *Maureen Vernal O'Brien*, it may well say *Dan O'Brien*. But it is Dan who grounds Maureen. It is he who counters her fantasy with logic, her whimsy with practicality.

First, I suggested to Dan that I help. I immediately felt his hesitation. His eyes spoke to me in a glance: "A hardworking Minnesota farm boy doesn't need help with anything, right?" Wrong. I pushed harder by inviting Dan to my house one night when Mo was recovering at home. Sitting closely, I looked him in the eye and told him he needed help, that I knew what to do, and that I was willing to do it.

Away from the chaotic reality, we both temporarily allowed ourselves to realize the severity of Mo's illness. Tears welled up as we shared real and raw feelings that we couldn't exhibit in front of Mo. At that moment, we could be weak together. We paused to briefly realize the feelings of a husband terrified that he may lose his bride and a friend afraid to lose yet another too young. That pause grounded us at that moment, and then it was time to move forward with a plan.

Part one of the plan was to get permission from Dan to set up Mo's CaringBridge website. This step enabled a communication flow with family, friends, and supporters outside the immediate family. Even though it was hard for Dan to recognize the need for a tool he had never heard of before, he was open to learning more. Dusting off my black binder housing hundreds of printed pages of entries from my sister-in-law's CaringBridge site, I passed it to Dan.

Big pause.

Because Dan is a very thoughtful and patient guy, he seemed to have a hard time opening the binder. Maybe because he remembered the outcome of my sister-in-law's lung cancer years before . . . or maybe because this was now his reality . . . or maybe because he is so patient and thoughtful.

Pressing Dan through his discomfort, I assured him that CaringBridge would be a godsend for everyone who wanted to help Mo, for his family near and far, and for his bride. I offered to set up the site and maintain it, which seemed an unspoken question. Family member contributions, including his own, were welcome when he or his kids felt inclined to write. Dan's response was not an enthusiastic yes, but rather—in Dan O'Brien style—a quiet nod, signaling the green light I needed to get started.

Building the site became the top priority and gave me a meaningful focus. Dan wrote an incredibly touching and thorough introduction, summarizing Mo's story to date and providing the needed backstory for the site, which we saved to the top of the page so it was the first post a new visitor would see. Adding in design elements and photos prepared the site for the throngs of people waiting for information and a channel for them to tune in to Mo's evolving story. Fans were ready to cheer her on as the first quarter kicked off and our jerseys were still fresh.

CaringBridge became the channel to communicate Mo's status and family needs, as well as specific ways for people to help. We also discovered that quiet Dan had a lot to say about "Da Bride" and his deep love for her and his family. This free site (which operates via donations) was also great support for Mo's family and extended family. The online comments were recited to Maureen when she was not well enough to read them on her own. Once Maureen felt well enough, she started posting herself, giving a first-person voice to her progress. This step was therapeutic for the online community, Mo personally, and her family.

Mo's site is still active at https://www.caringbridge.org/visit/maureenobrien, with over 10,000 "visits" by followers of her page since it was established in 2016. It stands as a beautiful reminder of how people come together when invited. She continues to post regarding her annual follow-up visits, reminding us all that the story is never truly "over" for the patient, their family, and the inner circle. We, as caretakers and friends of the diagnosed, tend to mostly "check out" once the all clear has been given, once we have dropped off the casserole or done a good deed. With so many challenges in our world, donor fatigue is real and should be expected throughout a long illness.

Britta's Guide to Quarterbacking a Loved One's Diagnosis

If you or someone you love is dealing with a life-threatening diagnosis, you need someone in the QB role as soon as possible. It's best if that someone is not a direct family member; someone like an in-law or very good friend is preferred. The QB with just a tad of distance from blood relatives can navigate more effectively with fewer emotions and manage (mostly) outside of family politics. My belief is that family should be physically present for their loved ones as much as possible, so this QB role shifts many burdens away from the family.

When drafting your team, four major areas of care are needed. Let's call them the "Four Quarters of Support." Since Maureen is a *huge* Pittsburgh Steelers fan, it's fitting to think of her care in football terms. She would agree to whatever I asked if I were waving a Steelers' flag and wearing a Pittsburgh jersey. Lining up people in these positions and recognizing the roles they play while connecting and managing the workflow is the role of the QB. The earlier the QB can delegate tasks to responsible family members or friends, the more efficient and effective the care system works for everyone.

The Four Quarters of Support:

1. Establish and maintain two-way communications channels.

2. Organize food.

3. Be the gatekeeper for visitors.

4. Coordinate care (in-home and outside of the home for the patient and other family members).

First Quarter: Kick Off the Communications Channel

Once others learn someone special in their network is critically ill, the chaos and stress get amplified because people (the fans) want to be more than spectators. If you don't provide a game plan for them, these spectators will either hang back and feel helpless or huddle up and create their own plays with unintended consequences (good and bad). A person's circle of friends, well-meaning as they are, become hungry for information and, if not provided a communication channel, will forge their own or use back channels, which can create more problems. Without a plan, you'll end up with five lasagnas in one week, a phone that rings off the hook, guests at unwelcome hours, an exhausted family, and a pile of dishes to return.

CaringBridge is the perfect place to focus communications. As a centralized platform, it takes the pressure off the family to provide individual updates to others. It's a place for the community of care to connect with their loved ones and each other. And it's a way for someone experiencing a critical diagnosis to feel connected, supported, and loved from afar—a crucial factor in maintaining positivity and hope.

Second Quarter: Food Management

Kicking off the second quarter, the QB should focus on helping the family manage food. It is human nature to want to bring food, be physically present, and feel part of the care team. Mo's longtime next-door neighbor, Ellen Ball, stepped up early in Q2 with an offer to help and accepted the responsibility to coordinate meals. Ellen set up an account at Meal Train, an online tool people could use to schedule what food to bring to the O'Briens' home and when. Once Ellen had set up the site, all I had to do was post a link to Meal Train on CaringBridge, and like magic, the food train left the station. Ellen was a great help in taking on that critical role and making sure the delivered food got inside the house as well. The Meal Train is now connected to CaringBridge.

Food is fuel, and it is also a hassle to organize when a family member is critically ill. Meal contributions help the family reduce time and energy spent on grocery shopping, food preparation, and cleanup, lightening that burden. A reminder that the person who is ill is probably largely immobile, so limiting the amount of high-calorie "comfort foods" is advised.

Tips for Setting Up a Meal Train:

1. Inquire with family whether they'd like meals organized.

2. Identify and secure a tech-literate site administrator.

3. Set up an account at mealtrain.com.

4. Inquire with the family about any food allergies or special diets, and post these considerations clearly on Meal Train.

5. Ask the family how many meals they want to be delivered per week. From experience, about three times per week is plenty, as there are usually leftovers and times when the family is not home for dinner or wants a break. There is an interactive online meal calendar for easy online sign-up.

6. Request a variety of meal types—and post a reminder to cook healthy. Pasta sure is easy, and it also gets old for the family. You can even provide direction for days of the week (e.g., Monday is chicken, Wednesday is pork/beef, and Friday is fish or pasta) to avoid getting three pasta dinners in a week. The family will thank you for that level of detail.

7. Designate someone in the family or a close friend to help write thank-you notes or emails to those providing meals (if you want to take this on). It is nice but not necessary to send thank-you notes, so don't stress about it if this task gets left undone.

Here are a few tips for the families preparing to deliver meals:

1. Pack meals in disposable containers. It is a burden on the family to remember which dish came from which family, clean it, and get it back to its owner. Stockpiled disposable containers can be sent home with visitors to be used again, if someone is willing to get that organized.

2. Send enough food for leftovers or portions that can be frozen individually. Freezer food is a blessing in an emergency.

3. Add an inspirational card, prayer, or note with your meal letting the family know you are thinking of them.

Alternatives to Crowdsourcing Meals:

1. Try alternative food choices. A friend suggested Fox Valley Food for Health (FVFFH) after our Meal Train was up and running. This local nonprofit serves the western Chicago suburbs and promotes a nutrition-focused community that educates teens and serves those struggling with a health crisis. Not only does FVFFH have a sound mission and model of education and service, but they also have volunteer "angels" who deliver healthy food in reusable containers. Once Maureen's family was approved (there is an interview and qualification process), the food was delivered to her home each week. This nutritious, cancer-fighting food helped supplement weekly food needs, so we reduced the Meal Train requests when interest was starting to decline. These healthy meals were even delivered to Mo during her weeklong hospital treatment when she had an ap-

petite. If there are similar organizations in your area, I'd highly recommend you consider using them. There was no fee, but donations are gladly accepted to pay it forward to the next family in need. Encouraging your friends to donate to this type of organization is also an option for involvement.

2. You can send the family a gift card for a local restaurant or online food service to use in a pinch or as part of a food strategy. Food delivery services like Grubhub, DoorDash, and Uber Eats bring the food right to their doorstep—a super convenience on the family's own time. This can be done right from Meal Train, or you can just purchase a gift card and send it to the home or email.

Halftime Pep Talk: Donor Fatigue

The four quarters are *long*. A halftime locker room chat about "donor fatigue" is where we'll focus now. Full disclosure: I have not officially researched this topic, but I have lived and observed it and want to note its effect.

Human nature is a funny thing—sometimes predictable and sometimes not—when it comes to supporting someone who is critically ill. The reality of our personal charity may be hard to acknowledge, but it's good to recognize it in black and white (or Steeler black and yellow in this case). Whether or not we are fully aware of our intentions and actions, we all compartmentalize and "rank" our relationships in some personalized way. We simply can't be present all the time for everyone for every life challenge.

I imagine relationships in three rings of support. Think of them as three concentric circles with each tier orbiting around the person who needs help.

Let's imagine it is you who is sick at the center. Your largest circle of friends and acquaintances comprises the biggest ring, orbiting the farthest away from you. This circle includes those in your life on whom you have made some level of impact through work, play, or volunteering. Members in this circle will want to "do something" to show they care and are thinking about you. This group likely practices the "one and done" approach, like signing up once for a Meal Train or sending a card or both. This level of interaction—not to sound crass—checks their "social conscience" box. They've done something to help. And they have. We need all the positive energy we can get during times of need from as many places and people as possible.

The middle circle includes your longer-term relationships and deeper levels of friendships with the person or family members. This team will dive in more quickly and stay the course longer than the outer circle. You can expect these people to want to visit in person, bring food, and help one or more times. After a few months, expect this group to slowly fall away but keep their presence known on CaringBridge.

Lastly, and closest to you, is the inner circle. This small group of family and very close friends will go into overtime to make sure all your needs are met. Again, this is a select group of people, many of whom will have one or more roles throughout the four quarters.

As a QB, being aware of these three circles at game time helps you plan and pace help for the duration of the four quarters. The more dire the diagnosis, the deeper the bench you'll need.

Third Quarter: Control Visitors

Communications are flowing, meals are being delivered, and well-meaning people are now just showing up at the patient's door to visit and drop things off, asking what they can do, etc.

Pro tip: Don't let other people's schedules dictate that of the person in need. Assign a resident family member the job of controlling whom, when, and how long visits take place.

The best way to go about this is to sit with the ill person early on with their address book or phone contacts and take notes on specific people they want to visit them. You know the folks in your life you can vomit on or ask to help you in the bathroom versus those who you'd enjoy a favorite recipe or short visit. Early in Mo's diagnosis, I sat down with her to, as the British would say, "sort it out," putting people into her version of the three concentric circles. This roster helped our team green-, yellow-, or red-light guests. It also determined whom she wanted at the hospital with her, as well as who visited during home care and "up" times in between treatments.

We all know people in our network who boost us up and those who exhaust us. Those talkers and those listeners. The "gatekeeper" role cannot be emphasized enough. After identifying those closest to Maureen, I emailed all of them to provide an update on Mo's condition, then invited them to CaringBridge and to a more intimate level of care or visitation as defined by Mo. Once a schedule was established, Jan, Mo's sister-in-law, and Lizzy, Mo's daughter, picked up and owned this role. Jan simply moved in with the family to help care for Mo so Dan could go to work, and Lizzy helped with household chores and writing thank-you notes. A schedule was also set up for hospital stays to allow for day and overnight companions; I was Wednesdays.

Remember to keep visits short; fifteen minutes is good. Visitors, especially those not in the center ring, wear out the patient.

Fourth Quarter: Coordinate Care

Like any household, the person who is critically ill has "chores" and family duties that will need to be assumed by others during this period—everything from taking care of pets to watering plants, carpooling children, and taking care of trash day, yard work, shopping, and housekeeping. Those chores don't just go away. A good QB recognizes the bench players willing to pick up things and asks them for specific help when needed. Family financials also need attention to make sure bills are being paid, especially if the sick person usually pays them. A debrief to go over what is due when and make sure insurance resources are in play are extremely important.

Mo's children were grown, so no carpooling was needed, but this is a major consideration for families with school-aged children. Friends are more than happy to help with this when asked specifically.

Next, a word about pets. Some pets are docile and comforting, and some go crazy every time the door rings and need to be let out constantly. And remember, some people are just not dog or cat people or may have allergies. If you think it is helpful, ask a friend close to the animal if they can help with walks or even be a foster family for periods.

The O'Brien's dog, Riley, is a "greetin' Wheaton" soft-coated terrier who just loved to get excited with visitors and needed lots of love and attention. The best scenario was to have Riley out of the house during Mo's intensive treatment, which was six months. Our family enjoyed having Riley at his "north-side home," and the O'Brien family had one less thing to worry about at home.

If a neighbor is looking for a way to help, mowing the lawn or shoveling the snow is a huge gift. If you're a neighbor to a person dealing with a critical diagnosis, either just do it, or let the family (or QB) know you are willing to do it for them. In Mo's case, I had a family anonymously pay a local landscape service to do their spring yard cleanup. And, as Mo's circles of friends are deeper than most and were looking for ways to stay engaged, I organized a "Garden Angels" event in late May.

A simple event post in CaringBridge asking for people to drop off and/or plant summer flowers in the O'Brien's yard was met with an almost overwhelming response. Dozens of flowers, cash to buy flowers, and friends with gloves and tools showed up in force to pot and plant all Mo's pots and gardens with annuals. That outward act of love and support was especially overwhelming for Mo. She was familiar with being the giver, not the receiver. And it was a gift that kept giving all during her recovery. (We did have to enlist the family to remember to water, so keep that in mind.) But for the people who dropped off flowers and participated in the day of yard work, it was also a special way to connect with each other and share stories of Mo. We even brought food and snacks to share with each other during the day. Being in community fed us as much as it did for the O'Briens. Keep in mind that when you provide concrete ways for others to participate in someone's care, you'll get a better response.

ILLUMINATIONS

How you show up for someone else is entirely your choice. You can choose which circle of care you want to be in and your level of participation. These are my two pieces of tangible advice for the person who needs help:

1. Find someone to serve as your QB (and have them read this chapter!).

2. Be specific about your offer of help.

The first item has been covered throughout this chapter. Call it what you like: *QB*, *point guard*, *project manager*, *shosben*, or coin your own term. Just know how critical it is in managing the four quarters (and, in the case of Maureen Vernal O'Brien, sweet victory!).

The second item is less intuitive. Our default response when offering help likely sounds like this: "Let me know if you need anything." Wrong. This puts the responsibility on the person in need. Instead, turn this around to offer something concrete that you are willing to do. Depending on which circle of care you choose, there is always something to offer: a meal, a carpool, yard work, and so on.

If a Meal Train is not set up yet, text, call, or email and say, "I'm bringing over dinner this week for your family. Is Tuesday or Wednesday better?" Then follow that up by asking how many people will be there for dinner and if there are any food allergies, then send it over hot in a disposable container.

Ready to do more? Be a QB, or if there is already a QB, contact them and ask to be assigned another team role. Just show up with your offer of help. (And if your loved one is anything like Mo, bring your Steelers pom-poms.) Illness is a major time-out, but with supportive fans in the stands, it's easier to get back on the field. We all only have so many quarters in our lives, and time spent helping a friend is never time wasted.

EVE OF THE PET SCAN

Journal Entry by Maureen O'Brien
May 16, 2016

It is the eve of my PET Scan. The process begins with an injection which will happen at 7 a.m. Cancer loves sugar, and this injection is a sugar substance that makes the cancer cells light up on the screen. The scan will take place an hour after the injection, and it will show how the treatment is working. I'll get the results on Friday.

I'm asking for your prayers. As you can imagine, there's a significant amount of angst, but I am trusting that God is already handling whatever is next. I would LOVE that "next" is a clean scan! :) Thanks in advance for storming heaven!

PET SCAN RESULTS

Journal Entry by Maureen O'Brien

May 20, 2016

Let me start by saying, "Thank you God!" While the scan was not completely clear as I had hoped, it showed a 90% reduction and NO NEW ACTIVITY! This really is great news! I am so incredibly grateful for your prayers and your encouragement! I will never be able to express in words the feelings of gratitude I have for you!

Monday starts round 4 of chemo. Five days at Northwestern, then two more rounds following that; each round 3 weeks apart.

Still a ways to go, but I am starting to see the light . . . it's not an oncoming train, is it?

CHAPTER 15

ELIZABETH GREEN

FRIEND, MASSAGE THERAPIST

I'm fairly certain most people don't have a friend who is skilled in massage. I'm absolutely certain that most people don't have a friend who is skilled in massage and willing to come to their home every day for seven months while they are in chemotherapy. But that's exactly what my friend Elizabeth Green did. Every day, she would come to my home (except the weeks that I was in the hospital) to massage my swollen legs and aching body on the little bed set up in my family room.

"Healing with prayerful hands" is the gift that Elizabeth offered. And what a gift it was. I am convinced that this alternative therapy contributed to my health and got me upright and able to move away from using a walker or wheelchair sooner than I otherwise would have. Elizabeth is a God-centered woman. Her hands and her prayers helped my healing, and I am grateful.

The Holy Spirit works in mysterious ways. This was certainly the case with how Maureen and I became friends. She first came to me as a massage client. I was a high school guidance counselor at the time, doing massage on the side. I have a spa-like space set up in my basement, complete with a hot tub. Maureen had her first massage with me as a very young mother. That seems like a lifetime ago.

Following our initial meetings, as our friendship grew, Maureen invited me to attend a local Bible study/prayer group. This was well over a decade ago. Maureen participated in our weekly group for a couple of years before her growing business and speaking engagement travel created an unpredictable schedule. It was also through this Bible study group that I learned Maureen had cancer and was requesting prayers from us. Quite simply, we all were in shock, stunned. Despite our initial disbelief, we prayed that this vibrant member of our group would find strength and be cured.

Feeling the need to do something after Bible study, I jumped in the car and headed to the hospital where she was being treated. Navigating the hallways of the new wing at Delnor, our local hospital, I located her room. The door was closed, so I did not enter. Unable to either enter her hospital room due to her treatment or fully comprehend the bigness of the challenge ahead, I felt helpless at that moment. Outside in the sitting area was Jan, Maureen's sister-in-law, who graciously filled me on her evolving status. All I could think was, *Oh my God, please heal her.* Walking back to my car, I kept thinking, *This could easily have been me . . . in the bed . . . so ill.*

From that point on, I started praying for Mo, her doctors, and her caregivers. Praying, for me, is like drinking water; my faith is something I can always rely upon to quench my thirst and a refuge for me to ask for help. Reflecting, I do remember Maureen's complaints of shoulder pain earlier that fall when she came to me for a massage. But there was a long gap in time between her last massage and me standing in the hospital outside her room. I knew instinctively that it would take all hands on deck, *including mine*, to heal her.

> *PRAYING, FOR ME, IS LIKE DRINKING WATER. MY FAITH IS SOMETHING I CAN ALWAYS RELY UPON TO QUENCH MY THIRST.*

Once Maureen was home from the hospital and could receive guests, I came to the house. Feeling called to help, I asked her directly, "What can I do for you?" and gave her several choices. I offered to rub her back, her feet, or her neck if massage would help. I left my offering and paused to listen for her response. Maureen accepted my invitation. Massage was something unique that I could do to help her and contribute to her care. Many others were bringing food, caring for her at home, or organizing things. My gift was literally in my hands, and now it was time for me to use them for the greatest good.

○   ○   ○

The role I played in Maureen's community of care was the gift of prayerful massage. During that first visit, I made a commitment in my mind to come every day when she was home in between chemo treatments. I never saw her in the hospital, only at home when she felt like having me visit and was receptive to hands-on healing. Through massage, I allowed God to use my hands to be His servant.

Coming to the O'Brien's home daily to give a massage, I was happy to be present and to be quiet so Maureen could unwind and be still. Keeping conversation to a minimum helped her be calm and relax; I told her it was OK to fall asleep, and many times she did. Many of my visits were spent quietly massaging with soft music playing in the background to help her relax and fall asleep. Sometimes she would talk a bit, but mostly, I tried to listen to the pain in her body through my fingers. I became sensitive to her body's signals, such as a twitch or pulling away from my hands when an area was hurting. I prayed the whole time I was present. I prayed for the power of the Holy Spirit to touch her body, her feet, her back, her shoulder. "Dear Lord, heal Maureen. Holy Spirit, heal Maureen." I witnessed the power of prayer and massage as part of Maureen's recovery.

Part of being in Maureen's community of care also meant meeting the wonderful family members and close friends who were at Maureen's home. And I wasn't just let in the front door; I was welcomed and made to feel part of their family. That welcoming spirit was good for me, as I felt like I belonged and wasn't intruding on their sacred family space. To this day, I feel a special family bond with the O'Brien children.

As the last days of recovery waned, I came to the realization that I gave my love, energy, and time through my hands. That's how I loved her. I prayed through my hands. And as the sixth and final treatment course was completed and the massages came to an end, I understood firsthand what a blessing it was for me to have been able to do something meaningful for another person. Prayerful massage was my gift to her, but the energy given and received was from the Holy Spirit—totally and 100 percent. To this day, I want the honor and glory and credit to go to the Holy Spirit and the Lord, Jesus Christ.

ILLUMINATIONS

I have two recommendations for anyone searching for ways to help another in need. They may sound simple, yet giving these gifts requires you to focus solely on the person in need and away from yourself. They can be done separately, but in my opinion, they are best when paired together.

First, **be present**. Be physically present for someone who needs you if that is possible. Just being there speaks volumes, even if you don't know what to say or don't say much. And be there when they need you, not just when it is convenient for you. Once you are physically present, then you are set up for number two.

Second, **listen**. Open your ears and your heart. Listen to the physical pain, the emotional pain, and the psychological pain. Sometimes, people just need to be heard. You may not have the answers, but for the person in need, having trusted friends who give them space to talk without judgment is a rare gift. And for the caregiver, just listening—real active listening—complements your physical presence.

FIRST DAY OF ROUND FOUR

Journal Entry by Maureen O'Brien

May 23, 2016

Cancer sucks. As I write, I am in my first day of Round 4 of chemo at NorthwesternHospital. I'm hooked up for five days to a 24-hour drip of chemo. As my friend Cheryl Juech says, "cancer is stupid."

I got great news from the PET scan last week about the 90% depletion in the cells in my body with no new activity of cancer cells. I should be doing back flips. Instead, I've been feeling really down, focused on how much more there is to go. For anyone who has been through this, is this normal? Is it just that I need to pause at this halfway point and refuel to continue the rest of the journey? I have talked to myself, yelled at myself, cajoled myself into feeling differently. The tears still come.

I would appreciate your thoughts, especially if you've been through it or have been close to someone who has. I'm counting on these feelings to be temporary, knowing that I will do whatever it takes to win this battle.

I am a warrior!

Flowers for Mo

CHAPTER 16

SUSAN MOODY ROMANO

FRIEND, NON-HODGKIN'S LYMPHOMA AND BREAST CANCER SURVIVOR

Many years ago, my friend Susan was diagnosed with stage 4 diffuse large B-cell non-Hodgkin's lymphoma—the very same diagnosis that I was receiving in 2016. Knowing this, and seeing that Susan was now healthy and whole, gave me hope.

*She became my North Star. I counted on her for advice and encouragement. I asked her (and still ask her) about things I was afraid to ask anyone else. She taught me about **"doing what needed doing"** and leaving the rest. Good advice then, good advice now.*

Oh, no! *Not Mo!*

Maureen ("Mo") and I go way back—a couple of our children attended preschool together in the nineties. We worshiped at the same church for years, and, as life would have it, I ended up moving just blocks from her after my divorce.

She is an unapologetically Jesus-loving, family-and-friend-centered, brilliant, kind, strong, creative woman with a penchant for style and lipstick too! When word came through that she'd been diagnosed with non-Hodgkin's lymphoma, my heart sank. I had survived a similar non-Hodgkin's lymphoma some years earlier, so I knew that I had to be her "look at me, there's life after this crap" survivor support. I also knew too well what she was in store for . . . and that I did not want to share. But she *would* survive. I could not—*would not*—allow myself to imagine it any other way.

> I HAD SURVIVED A SIMILAR NON-HODGKIN'S LYMPHOMA, SO I KNEW THAT I HAD TO BE HER SURVIVOR SUPPORT. I ALSO KNEW TOO WELL WHAT SHE WAS IN STORE FOR.

Britta McKenna, a good friend of Maureen's, was my contact person to learn what she was going through and what I could do. One of the highlights of the encouragement organized to lift Maureen's spirit was a Garden Angels day. A large group of us showed up at her house and took over the entire yard, trimming, edging, mowing, planting, weeding, brightening up, and lovingly beautifying it for her. At that point of her treatment, she was spending large parts of each day resting inside and looking out over the yard. We wanted to make sure that what she saw was not only exceptional beauty but also love and encouragement, and that we were *all in* to support her through this journey and beyond.

The Garden Angels day hit her hard. Maureen was so overwhelmed by all of us showing up that she had to leave. She is forever grateful and thankful . . . but it was just too much. She can share with you her "why," but we did what we did because we knew it was going to help her through.

I prayed a lot for Maureen to be blessed with complete remission and a long, long life. I also became more active with the Leukemia & Lymphoma Society, raising funds through local events as a host and a guest. It is what I felt I could do to continue to support her.

The community of "Mo Lovers" is far and wide, extending to reaches of the world that I will never know. But within our area, the Fox Valley community circle of family and friends, just knowing what was being done via physical acts, emotional support, fund-raising, and prayer on our knees loudly and quietly is only a testament to Mo and her love of others. Thankful *yes*! She is the best!

ILLUMINATIONS

I have learned and would offer several things to others who are going through difficult times, whether it be it a life-altering diagnosis or some other trauma:

1. Do not say to a person or their family member, "Call me if you need anything!" Rarely will they call. Instead, call and ask what you can provide that day or week to help on any level. A meal? A visit? A run to the store? Just a listening ear over the phone? Do not wait for them to reach out.

2. The following suggestion may not work for everyone, but my sister is so good at asking this question during dire times: "What is your biggest fear?" Once I talked about the "it," the journey became less scary. In total honesty, in my own battles with cancer, often the answer was that my greatest fear is an early death. So we talked about that. Sometimes it was about my adult children and what they might be suffering through. We discussed that too. Know who it is that you are asking; it might work for them too.

3. Speaking of fear, I had one very good friend who did not reach out to me during my cancer journey until it was almost over. When she finally resurfaced in my life, I asked her where she had been. Her eyes filled with tears. She shared that she had allowed the fear of seeing me in a weakened condition prevent her from reaching out, knowing that if I could be so sick, she might be able to get that sick too. It was just too hard for her, so she avoided me. It burdened her heart. From that, I learned that we can't let our fears dictate what we do or don't do in caring for others. The old motto still holds true: "*Just do it!*"

CALLING ALL ANGELS

Journal Entry by Britta McKenna

May 23, 2016

Calling all angels with a green thumb,

If you are available and looking for a way to show Mo some love, we are organizing a "Flowers for Mo' drive and planting this weekend. The theme is an "All-American summer," with red, white and blue flowers (shade and sun) to help us celebrate the 100th anniversary of the establishment of Flag Day. You can donate a flat of flowers, hanging basket and/or help us plant. The weather looks a bit 'iffy' for later this week, so let's say we are planting this Saturday from 1-3 p.m. and Sunday is the rain date at the same time. Don't live nearby? Leave a message with your email and send me a check and I'll be your personal shopper.

If you can donate flowers, please reply to this post and let us know what you are bringing. If you can't make it Saturday at 1, then feel free to drop off flowers on their front porch this Friday anytime or Saturday morning so we have our stock in hand. If you can help us plant, plan to arrive by 1 pm on Saturday and bring your hand tools if you have them. Beverages and snacks are optional. Contact my cell phone if you have any questions or want to confirm if we are working if weather looks threatening. I'll post a go/no go message on the thread Saturday morning.

Here's what we need:

- Planting angels—many
- Hanging basket of red geraniums (2)
- Hanging basket of red, white, and or blue impatience (2)
- 6 spike plants
- 9 potato plants
- 9 vinca vines
- 1 flat white impatience
- 1 flat red impatience
- 1 flat blue impatience (hmmm, do they make blue?) (or other flower)

Hope to see many of you this weekend.

Please remember to post a reply to this thread if you can bring something (and be specific, so we know).

Warm Regards,
Britta McKenna

CHAPTER 17

BETH SULLIVAN

FRIEND, CANCER SURVIVOR

> Beth and I have been connected for over thirty years. When we met, she was the high school athletic director, and I was the head cheerleading coach. That seems like eons ago. Probably because it was! Beth came to the hospital often during my week-long treatments. She exemplified **"being a good listener,"** so it's no surprise that that's her advice.
>
> Listening well is critical when you are part of a community of care. Not prescribing or offering any "shoulds," just listening well.

I remember the day that I heard of Mo's diagnosis. I was working in my home when I received the text message. Shortly after, I went outside and ran into one of my neighbors, who was part of the same church community as Mo. She relayed that the parish had requested prayer for Mo and, knowing that Mo was a friend, wondered if I knew any details of what was happening.

My heart immediately hurt. The range of emotions I felt was all over the place. I knew I had to do something. This is where this always gets so complicated. You don't know what to do. You know that your friend or family member has a tremendous number of appointments and tests. You know they're managing emotions, and you don't want to "bother them." But gosh, you just want to get *to* them to offer some support. I've been through this cancer diagnosis with Mo, my sister-in-law, who was diagnosed with leukemia, and several dear friends who have been lost recently to cancer. I am a breast cancer survivor as well.

> THE RANGE OF EMOTIONS I FELT WAS ALL OVER THE PLACE. I KNEW I HAD TO DO SOMETHING. THIS IS WHERE THIS ALWAYS GETS SO COMPLICATED. YOU DON'T KNOW WHAT TO DO.

As Mo traveled this journey, one of the most poignant times for me was when I visited her in the hospital. I knew she was sick. In addition to the cancer and all that goes with that, she had contracted the flu and pneumonia. I talked with her daughter in the hallway and quickly realized how bad the situation was. When I finally saw Mo, she was battling a high fever and was unable to speak. I simply could not believe this was happening to my friend. Even though I have walked this journey myself and watched other family and friends walk their own journeys, I felt incompetent and helpless.

To this day, I don't feel like I did much of anything to help get Maureen or anyone else I've known with this diagnosis upright! I remember visiting her in her backyard. Mo has a beautiful home with an inviting swimming pool. One day, she was sitting in the shade by the pool and was crying. She had had intestinal trouble from recent chemotherapy and was embarrassed by it as it related to my visit. I did nothing but listen. She simply needed to "get it out" and talk about this part of the disease. I felt again unable to help. Simply listening didn't seem so important, but my presence and listening were what *she needed* on that day. You can never help the patient with *all* the dark times, but you can provide a fresh face and listening ear, always!

My own cancer journey *all* happened during the COVID-19 pandemic. That is a chapter, if not a book, in and of itself. It's hard to put into words the wonderful care I received from doctors, nurses, receptionists, technicians . . . health care professionals. *They* made my journey doable.

In tandem with telling important stories like these, I pray that one day we will develop the ability to defeat cancer through research and development. In the meantime, decide that you can and will contribute some of your love and light to another person's community of care.

YOU CAN NEVER HELP THE PATIENT WITH
ALL THE DARK TIMES, BUT YOU CAN PROVIDE
A FRESH FACE AND LISTENING EAR.

ILLUMINATIONS

I've had many years of practice with cancer. What I would recommend to other caregivers is this: **Remember the little things.**

You never expect a cancer diagnosis, so the day that it comes, there are many things that the patient and family must do to *live*! As supporters of the patient, we can ensure that there's a meal ready to pop in the oven when the patient comes home from the hospital or therapy, the house is clean, the family pet is taken care of, cards are in the mail. We, as a community of care, can provide invaluable actions of support by helping with all of these things.

Another critical area: checking in on the caregivers—a lot! I have not been a direct caregiver, but I have watched Mo's husband, kids, and friends, and I've witnessed my own brother as the primary caregiver for my sister-in-law as she dealt with leukemia. For me, watching my brother take on all the responsibilities of caregiving was more difficult than I had imagined. He aged right before my eyes, but he did not miss a beat when it came to advocacy for his wife, and he never left her side. Even when we tried to get him to leave the hospital for a good night of sleep in a hotel, he did not want to leave.

The caregivers are the ones to watch as they navigate a loved one's terrible disease. The doctors, nurses, and other health personnel pay attention to the patient, but seldom do we listen to, watch, and check in on the caregivers. Family and friends also struggle with not knowing how to help. These emotions are real and, if left unchecked, can create more sickness!

Technology has become an important part of caregiving. I've seen applications that organize meals for family members and platforms that allow the patient or other family members to communicate, en masse, information related to the illness and care plan. My family leaned heavily on one of these platforms when my sister-in-law got sick. She was able to muster the energy to provide daily updates. Again, this helped *her*, but it was also a huge help to the many supporters who waited for daily updates.

OVERWHELMED BY YOU!

Journal Entry by Maureen O'Brien

May 24, 2016

When Britta told me that flower angels were coming this weekend, I was overwhelmed with emotion!

I love my backyard, it's where we spend the entire summer. It's always been a place of beauty, friends gathering, good wine, lots of laughter, campfires, a meditation space. It's barren right now; one more reminder of my limitations. I cannot tell you the lift I'm feeling from knowing color is coming. Life and growth will come back to the yard, a metaphoric reminder for me and my own life.

In Britta's note, she said snacks are "optional" on Saturday. Seriously? You're coming to the O'Briens! There WILL be snacks. Beer, wine, water, sandwiches, pop, chips, whatever else we can pull together. It's the smallest thanks we can provide. I hope I feel well enough to squeeze on each of you! Please know that my immune system is low, so if you have sniffles at all, we'll hug from a distance!

Knowing that you're coming this weekend has made these next four days in the hospital more tolerable. Thank you. You have my heart and deepest gratitude. I love you!

GARDEN ANGELS DESCEND

Journal Entry by Britta McKenna
May 28, 2016

A flock of Garden Angels (about 25) toiled in the soil to plant flowers for Mo. Some enterprising Angels trimmed hedges, weeded and beautified. It was a wonderful community of people who wanted to help and just needed a way. Thanks to others who dropped off flowers, pots, potting soil, and plants on Friday or who came earlier in the week to pot or weed. We are grateful for each one of you, some who haven't seen Mo for a decade or more.

Mo was overcome by emotion to see everyone arriving and sends her love and thanks to you all. For it is through the prayers, love, and support from family and friends that continues to be the strength both needed and appreciated. Since I can't post all the pictures on this post, I'll comment a number of times with more photos and will post the photo album on Maureen's Facebook page.

Have a wonderful Memorial Day weekend.

HOMESTRETCH

Journal Entry by Britta McKenna

June 5, 2016

It is great to see the light at the end of the tunnel and have support getting to the finish line. It is also a time of being weary of
the process, of being sick and of being sick of being sick and
wanting things to be normal again. This week Mo was strong
enough to go into the Global office for a couple hours to check
in and is slowly re-engaging with "life" that has been waiting for
her. And life can be overwhelming when you peek behind the
curtain to see what may lie ahead when there are so many un-
certainties. The O'Brien Family is ever grateful for all the love and
support that has sustained their journey. Last Saturday's Garden
Angels planting was a wonderful display that Mo and her family
are enjoying each day. Thank you all—whether you have brought
a meal, prayed, sent a card, helped plant flowers, or provided
help in any way. Please continue to pray for strength and total
recovery. Maureen starts Round 5 (out of 6) next Monday, June
13, and if all goes well the final round starts July 4—her Independence week!

IMPORTANT: Looking for meal angels to sign up on Meal Train. Dinners are needed starting next week through end of chemo and Ellen has updated the dates on Meal Train. Remember to sign up to bring a dinner to the O'Briens.

Blessings on the journey. Britta

APPRECIATING THE WORK OF YOUR HANDS

Journal Entry by Maureen O'Brien

June 7, 2016

I cannot begin to thank you for the pure joy I have experienced from the work of your hands in my garden, and the work of your hearts in my life.

The Saturday that the Garden Angels came, I was so overtaken with emotion that I could not stay at the house. I'm sorry for that. I wanted to be able to thank you in person, to hug you, to put voice to the feelings that are so deep within me. And yet I could not stay. I was aching inside. I feel like I'm rambling as I write. I hope in some way you can forgive me and understand.

I am getting stronger every day. Stronger isn't always easier. Stronger has also meant for me that now I have the capacity to look at my business from which I've been sidelined from for 5 months. Worry takes over. Will we be OK? Will I be able to rebuild? Will the business come back? What can I do? Will we overcome this financial hit?

None of this can I control. I think that's the hardest part and the biggest lesson for me. We have so very little control over our lives, thinking that we can package life up in a perfect box and stack it neatly with methodical precision. I can't give energy to this worry right now.

I would ask that if any of you have advice or coaching for me, I'd absolutely welcome it. I'd also ask that if you have an opportunity to hire a speaker or if you have connection to a major corporation where diversity and inclusion is a priority, you remember me and the Global Women's Leadership Forum. Of course, from the construction (O'Brien & Son, Inc) side of the business, if you need siding, soffit, fascia, window trim . . . we'd appreciate the chance.

Thank you for hearing me, allowing me a place to share my worries, and for loving me regardless of my crazy.

Round 5 starts Monday. I am ready.

READY FOR ROUND FIVE

Journal Entry by Britta McKenna

June 12, 2016

Maureen is ready to start Round 5 chemo at Northwestern tomorrow morning. It's time to rev up prayer warriors! Mo is rested up and has been cheering on her Pittsburgh Penguins. Lizzy is on a mission trip this week. Riley is at Camp McKenna, and Mo's bags are packed ready for Dan to escort her to the hospital in the morning. A report to the flower angels—flowers are filling out in the pots nicely! Thanks to all of you who have signed up to bring a meal to the family. All dates in June except this Friday have been signed up for—thank you! Mo comes home from chemo this Friday, so if you are able to greet her with a meal (or dates in July as well), sign up at her MealTrain.com website.

Make it a good week.

CHAPTER 18

DONNA WIKERT

FRIEND, SORORITY SISTER

*As friends and college sorority sisters, Donna and I have been through a lot. We were both maids of honor in each other's wedding. Donna went on to study Reiki and massage as well as other healing modalities. Her belief in seeing it first, or **"envisioning a positive outcome,"** is something I believe too. I hope this is or will become your belief!*

God bless every individual who picks up this book looking for answers, support, and inspiration. I pray that you find it. A diagnosis of cancer is one that affects not only the patient but, in a very distinctive way, every individual whose lives the patient has touched.

We are unique individuals traveling separate paths in this world. Where we are with our own life's journey will likely determine our response to hearing a dreaded diagnosis of cancer in a loved one.

Many times in my life, I could have curled up in a ball, or I could choose to persevere. Yes, it's a choice, but many times we are too weak to decide. So what can we do? How do we find our strength? For me, it was God answering my continual prayers, which gave me the strength to persevere through the darkest times. As I saw the light at the end of my own tunnels, I wanted to shout it out from the rooftops! I made a conscious decision in those times to provide more inspiration for others than I ever had in the past. I began to intentionally pay blessings forward each day, consciously choosing to live in a state of love and gratitude.

> HOW DO WE FIND OUR STRENGTH?
> FOR ME, IT WAS GOD ANSWERING MY
> CONTINUAL PRAYERS WHICH GAVE ME
> THE STRENGTH TO PERSEVERE THROUGH
> THE DARKEST TIMES.

I began my career in accounting, but through God's divine intervention, I transitioned into massage therapy as well other healing modalities. This God-inspired profession is my passion in life! My intention for you will be coming from the inspiration which God has given me. It all blossoms from unconditional love.

Maureen and I grew up in the Pittsburgh area. We both love the Steelers. Is there anyone in Pittsburgh (or the *world*) who doesn't? We met in college and immediately became great friends. We were involved in each other's lives throughout college and into our marriages. We are sisters of the same sorority, which proved to be a solid foundation of friendships I have cherished for over forty years. As life moved on and we began raising our families, our sorority kept in touch through social media sites. I was quite involved with my family and career. As there is in any life, there was a plethora of ups and downs. I noticed that my interests were changing. I became immersed in the study of my faith and eventually removed myself from all social media sites. It felt so right. All was calm. And then . . . *bam!*

My phone provided news I never expected to hear. It was a diagnosis, cancer in my friend. I got the news through a sorority group text. The same message asked that we not contact Maureen or her family due to this overwhelming diagnosis. They were preparing for what was ahead. The request was that we not visit until the family knew more and Maureen was stronger.

What? How could this be? Everyone was running in different directions trying to address this diagnosis of what was initially thought to be a torn rotator cuff in Maureen's shoulder. We were told communication from a designated family member would be provided to our sorority sister Anne. She would then communicate the information to our sorority. And just that fast, life had changed for so many people.

My first response to hearing of Maureen's diagnosis was a feeling of helplessness. It's my nature to hug, squeeze, and console those in need. But Maureen was ten hours away. Communication was going to be trickled down from the family. I couldn't even remember the last time she and I had spoken. There I was, off social media where everyone was sharing their thoughts and feelings about this experience. I felt disconnected. How could I help Maureen from a distance? I immediately fell into prayer. I sent her distant healing energy. I also pray the rosary. Catholics understand how "The Mysteries of the Rosary" envelop *every* life situation. I began adding Maureen to my list of intentions when dedicating the prayers of the rosary.

My faith has taught me the power of prayer surpasses all adversity. Blessings can be found in every situation if you *look* for them. This is a difficult concept when adversity touches someone you love. We can talk the big talk, but it was time for me to walk the walk. I knew Maureen would need hope. She and her family have a solid foundation of faith, and I knew everyone was holding Maureen up in prayer as I was. That was not only a blessing to Maureen; it was a comfort to me.

> IT'S HARD TO GIVE UP WHAT WE CONSIDER CONTROL, BUT WE HAVE NO CONTROL. ALL WE HAVE IS HOPE AND THE ABILITY TO PRAY.

It was now time for me to place my trust in God. I had to trust. I had to have no doubt that God would heal her. It's hard to give up what we consider control, but we have no control. All we have is hope and the ability to pray. For me, hope rests in prayer.

There are so many ways one can increase healing energy. Did you know your thoughts are energy? Well, they are. Every time you think or speak a positive statement, that's the energy you draw to yourself and to those you are thinking of or speaking to. The same goes for negative thoughts and words. I did not allow even one negative thought to enter my mind regarding Maureen's healing and survival. Not one. I chose to pray for healing, and I asked for God's will to be in alignment with my prayers.

Intention is everything. If your intention is for a loved one to be healed, thank God now for their healing even though that healing has not yet taken place. Always keep your prayers positive. Never allow doubt to enter your mind. Raise your love energy—it exceeds all boundaries!

As the days went by, we were all hungry for news. Some of our local sorority sisters in the Pittsburgh area gathered for lunch. We brought gifts of love to send to Maureen that we hoped might also provide some joy and laughter. Our sisterhood relationships were strengthened as we shared stories about Maureen and prayed together for her strength to prevail. Here was another blessing.

Communication with Maureen was limited through the seven months of her chemotherapy. She was frail and weak. The CaringBridge community became a wonderful source of information, connection, and inspiration. In time, the doctors and family allowed visitors. It was decided that nine of us, all from the sorority, would make a road trip from Pittsburgh to Chicago. Our sorority friendships were forty-plus years old. One of our travelers even made a three-hour bus ride to Pittsburgh so that she could be part of our adventure to Maureen's home. We purchased sorority shirts so we could celebrate our sisterhood when we were finally with Maureen.

The ten-hour ride was hilarious. Our stomachs ached from all the laughter. Imagine, five adult women in each car, cackling, singing, laughing the entire way! Pure joy. We met up at times with the gals in the other car, shared our stories, and laughed even more. In the middle of this difficult and dark time, we were experiencing such a blessing. The true friendship and love in that car helped us release the pent-up emotions we were all experiencing. I'm pretty sure we also solved most of the world's problems along the way! And the entire time, laughter—so much laughter. It was healing for all of us. Amid such adversity, this road trip was yet another blessing.

The anticipation and excitement of seeing and hugging Maureen were overwhelming. I simply wanted to hold on for a lifetime, like I'd wanted to ever since first hearing of her diagnosis of non-Hodgkin's lymphoma. The outpouring of emotion covered all of us. One by one, we hugged and squeezed Maureen. We cried. We sat in her home and surrounded each other with unconditional love. Whatever differences we may have had in the past were now long forgotten. They just dissolved. We were connected on a universal level of unconditional love. There was no gift greater than seeing the transformation in Maureen as she went from near death to full of life.

As we continued to talk, I wanted to move the conversation from cancer to life moving forward. I could see that rehashing the cancer experience was troubling for Maureen. It isn't always easy to do, but it's important to keep conversations positive and moving forward, especially when dealing with adversity. I'm not suggesting that you not address the past; you just don't want to get stuck there.

Ask your loved one if they want to talk or share their experience. If they don't, that's OK. Just let them know you are listening and will make yourself available if they want to share thoughts or feelings in the future. Try to stay in the present moment as much as you are able. Remain positive. Remember, it's always about them, not about you. If your loved one does want to share, you can show support without words. Listen attentively for the emotions "behind" the words. Keep eye contact, and know that it's OK to share a comfortable silence together. Try not to give advice unless your loved one asks for it. It's not your experience. There are no "shoulds." Just be.

IT'S IMPORTANT TO KEEP CONVERSATIONS POSITIVE AND MOVING FORWARD, ESPECIALLY WHEN DEALING WITH ADVERSITY. I'M NOT SUGGESTING THAT YOU NOT ADDRESS THE PAST; YOU JUST DON'T WANT TO GET STUCK THERE.

That evening during dinner, Maureen shared a family tradition. She passed around the chalice she and Dan had used at Mass on the day of their wedding. This chalice had now become the family blessing cup. Each one of us held that cup and shared what we were grateful for. This was an extraordinary blessing for each of us. It filled us with love and gratitude. The experience truly was a gift from her—a ritual that we could all take home and incorporate into our own lives. Yet another blessing.

ILLUMINATIONS

I believe that God sends angels, but they rarely come from the sky. Most are right here on earth. You can be that angel for a loved one in need. It's a privilege to ease the burdens of another. The return is tenfold. And you don't have to be physically present to make a positive difference in a loved one's life when distance separates you from them. There are so many ways to impact your loved one, even from a distance.

Thank God for your loved one's healing every day, even before the healing occurs.

Pray that God's will is in alignment with your prayers. Your loved one will feel the positive energy that you send their way. Prayer matters, and it's incredibly powerful. You can focus on rote prayer, meditate, utilize prayer beads, or simply talk to God . . . the *way* you pray for your loved one isn't what matters. What matters is that you *do* pray.

Look for blessings even in adversity. Embrace them! While Maureen walked this grueling walk, she continued to touch the lives of so many during her own adversity. She exuded gratitude.

One clear blessing is that today, Maureen is in remission. Her willingness to bring her story forward is a blessing to others who will learn today that they might walk a similar path. From darkness comes light. Another blessing.

As you think about your loved one, think and affirm positive statements. Hold your intention for their good health, their health care professionals, their physical well-being. Remain in a state of love and gratitude for as many moments of the day as you can.

Demonstrate that love by sending cards, texts, notes, books, emails, or tokens of love in which your loved one has an interest. Show up when you're able. Don't ask to help—find *something* you can help with, and just do that. This is the time to expand your vision and really see what someone who is struggling might need.

Be patient with yourself and your loved one. If possible, help your loved one to stay active and engaged in what's possible. Minimize cancer conversations (unless they initiate them). Remember, your loved one may have slowed down, but they have not stopped. Help them continue to live, laugh, and love! As you do, our tribe will continue to hold you and your loved one in our hearts.

TOUGH WEEKEND. TOUGH DAY

Journal Entry by Maureen O'Brien

June 14, 2016

So far, I have not experienced a lot of anger in this journey. I know that emotion is a significant part for some, but probably when anger was given out, I was in the tears line six or seven times. This weekend changed that for me.

Friday night, Dan was sleeping on the couch and I in the bed that we have set up in the family room. I had just fallen to sleep when Dan started to scream, "Help . . . Help!" I was terrified. I jumped up and turned on the light. I could not wake him up. Frantically, and after much shaking, he came to. He could not remember what he was dreaming about and saw no humor in my making him stand up, walk around, touch his finger to his nose while standing on one foot, and spelling lunch backwards. I was checking for a stroke. I'm not even sure any of those are signs of a stroke, but I needed him to do something. Never in the 33 years that we have been together has this happened. It confirms my suspicions that even though Dan insists he's doing fine, he is quietly carrying this stress, and trying to handle it on his own. That's what this disease does. It taunts every single person involved and laughs at the chaos it creates. Dan is scared, but he will never, ever tell you that.

So I have another ask...I would ask that with Father's Day coming, you support Dan with a card or encouraging note. I've been flooded with inspiring cards from you which have lifted me up immensely. Dan is a wonderful father. He is also proving to be an extraordinary caregiver, feeding me, carrying me to the bathroom when I could not carry myself, handling all my medications, etc. It's a lot while holding down a full-time job. Thanks to Ed Curtis at West Rock for your kindness, latitude, and understanding in this difficult time for our family. Your leadership inspires that there truly are people who value human capital in organizations as well as the bottom line. We are grateful.

Could you find time to send Dan a note? If not, send up a prayer.

My anger was propelled even farther today when we arrived at the hospital, there were no orders of admission for me. I'm sure you understand that there's a bit of angst just getting one foot in front of the other to face a hospital stay, knowing you are going to be hooked up to a 24/7 poisonous drip and in a hospital bed for 5 consecutive days. There was a communication problem somewhere, but it was not clear where the fracture was, and no one was taking responsibility. Doesn't really matter. I just wanted them to fix it and get me started. The later we start, the later I go home on Friday.

After about an hour, I finally got into my room. It was 1 p.m. before I got hooked up to my first bag-Benadryl, which helps with side effects of chemo, I had on a pretty thick robe so I was unaware that the IV tube was leaking, and the Benadryl was not making it to its final destination. The nurses could not determine how much (if any) of the medicine made it into my system, so the decision was to run it again. It was now 3:30 p.m. and I AM angry, mostly because, one more time, it's so very clear that I have little or no control over any of this. I'm sure that is the lesson. **I am not in control.**

Happy Father's Day to all fathers. I hope it's a relaxing, grace filled day for all of you. Hug your kids. Kiss you wife. Use your words. THOSE are some things **you CAN control.**

Still facing forward,
MO

ROUND 5 IS IN THE BOOKS

Journal Entry by Britta McKenna

June 18, 2016

A short note to share the news that Mo finished Round 5 of chemo yesterday and is resting at home. She now has two weeks to rebuild her strength and to prepare for round 6, the finale that starts on July 4, her Independence week. Happy Father's Day to all you dads out there. Enjoy time with your family on this glorious weekend ahead.

Keep up the prayers as we are in the home stretch!

CHAPTER 19

TERRY BOZZA

FRIEND, NEIGHBOR

> As were many of our family and friends, Terry Bozza was states away when I received my diagnosis. We in Illinois, she in Florida, distance felt insurmountable and increased the feelings of helplessness. Terry's advice for **"long-distance assistance and care"** shows clearly that there is space for everyone and that all actions of care are impactful.

I can remember exactly how I met Mo the first time. She and Dan own a condo in a neighborhood in Florida where my husband and I were looking to purchase our retirement home. We were driving slowly down a street in this neighborhood when we happened to see a woman coming from the community pool. She was loaded down with towels, a beach bag, and floaties in her hands. My husband Bob and I debated which one of us would roll down the window to ask if she knew of any homes for sale. I volunteered because this was too much like asking for directions for Bob. Mo replied that she knew of none in the area, but perhaps her home would be on the market soon. She asked if we wanted to see it. Just like that, our friendship was launched.

Mo ultimately decided not to sell her home, and we bought a home within walking distance of hers. From that chance meeting, a wonderful new friendship was born. Whenever she was in town, she would gather everyone she knew for whatever activities the neighborhood club was promoting. If there were none, she would create her own.

It was during one of her visits that Mo had organized a dinner out with some friends. It was a lovely evening. She happened to tell us that she was having some difficulty with her shoulder. Bob had had rotator cuff surgery, and we "diagnosed" her injury as such, giving her advice as to the type of PT she should have. We made plans about what we would do when she returned. Hugs and kisses followed as we bade them goodbye. She and Dan left the next day for Chicago.

I don't remember the time lapse from that evening, but I remember a mutual friend, Carole, came to my door. When I opened the door, her sweet smile and hello gave way to tears. Through her sobs, I learned that what we thought was a rotator cuff problem was stage 4 lymphoma. I stood, unable to comprehend what I had just heard. How could this be? I had just seen her! We'd talked and laughed the night away. I was dumbfounded.

Finally getting my wits about me, I invited Carole in to talk. As we sat down, she told me all she knew. The truth was, at that point, we did not have much information. Distance made it so much more difficult. We spent the rest of the visit crying and trying to console each other. Then the questions started: Should we call or text? Surely all of Mo's friends would be calling and texting. Would that be too much for the family? But it would be worse if we didn't text, wouldn't it? To say that I felt lost and confused is an understatement. The miles between us shifted from being difficult to feeling impossible, and I had a sense of deep helplessness.

> WE SPENT THE REST OF THE VISIT
> CRYING AND TRYING TO CONSOLE EACH
> OTHER. THEN THE QUESTIONS STARTED.

The next day, I decided that I would text Mo, and if she were up to it, she would respond. If not, I knew I would find another way to learn how she was doing. I was not sure how, but I just knew that I would tenaciously pursue it. I needed her to know that she was not on this path alone and, although I was miles away, I would be on the path with her in spirit. I sent her a text. She responded about her prognosis and asked for prayers. I don't mean to minimize the effect of prayers, but I wanted to *do* something that she could actually *see*!

Not long after Mo's initial text to me, another text came saying that she would not be up to texting anyone for a long while. She was weak and getting weaker, but her progress could be followed on CaringBridge, which is a platform for those undergoing a traumatic health circumstance and its treatments.

I was so relieved to learn this. At least now I could follow her progress and not feel as though I were intruding during the family's difficult time. CaringBridge would be monitored by Mo's very good friend, Britta. Britta was diligent about posting Mo's progress. I don't remember how often Britta posted, but I do know her posts were detailed and most welcomed. She told of Mo's triumphs and setbacks, and I felt as though I was there celebrating with her or consoling her. From time to time, Mo's husband Dan posted on CaringBridge and gave the family's perspective of her journey.

Besides chronicling her progress, Britta organized meals to be taken to the family. Mo has numerous friends, and I guessed that most, if not all, of the meals would be graciously made and delivered to their home. But still . . . *I wanted to do something.* Of course, cooking a meal was out of the question, but what could I do that would, in some small way, take a small burden from the family? I researched restaurants in the area where the O'Briens live, and I decided the chain restaurants were a safe bet. Every month or so, I would send a gift card to the O'Briens from Chili's or Panera. Doing this, I felt like I was a part of the essential community of care supporting Mo as she faced horrific challenges. It was my hope that in some small way, it would represent my care, love, and concern for this wonderful woman and her family.

ILLUMINATIONS

The cancer patient and family are thrown into a chasm, and I can only imagine the feelings that bombard them daily. They need a "Britta" in their court who can be the liaison between family and friends and who can coordinate delivering meals, giving rides to the doctor, chauffeuring children, and distributing information to friends. Even though a cancer patient cannot respond to your texts, they need to know that they are not alone and that they are in your thoughts and prayers. And if, like me, you are miles apart, you can make your presence felt by sending an occasional gift card to a restaurant or even a housecleaning service.

Finally and most importantly, the patient *and their family* need you to be present to them. This might not be a matter of being physically present, but be "present" in a way that lets them know you care about, love, and support them. This is the greatest gift you can give them in this, their darkest hour. You have an opportunity to be light. Take the opportunity.

LONGING FOR THE MUNDANE

Journal Entry by Maureen O'Brien

June 20, 2016

I am glad to have Round 5 behind me. One more starting July 4. Can't come soon enough.

This past weekend, I struggled with envy for all the things that seem so easy to others; the ability to drive a car down the street, walk the dog or pull weeds in the yard. I never appreciated these things. I long for them now. It's hard not to look at others with envy. Life seems so simple outside of this one. I'm envious that other people's lives are continuing as normal when mine has paused in this chaos. I find myself thinking continuously about the future which creates great fear in me. I know that none of us are assured of a moment beyond this one. Yet, I worry about us financially. I worry about Dan. Will this disease destroy everything we've built because I'm not at peak performance right now? These fears haunt me, and I am struggling to stay in the peace of God, trusting that there is a plan and that all shall be well. I'm beginning to lose confidence in my own abilities. That is, I think, the biggest fear of all.

Again, I appreciate so much being able to share here. It feels safe. Non-judged. I don't know if I'm supposed to write about this in a bigger way—or what I'm called to be doing with this experience. It's so incredibly hard. I am open to all spirit energy. I do hope that this experience is able to help others, and if you have ideas for me, or know someone who might, I'm wide open.

I don't know how to do this any better than I am. I would encourage you, however, to give thanks for even the most mundane in your life. When you get in your car, give thanks. When you take your dog for a walk, give thanks. Don't curse those nasty weeds, give thanks. Your life is a blessing. Appreciate it. Especially the mundane.

HOLDING TIGHT

Journal Entry by Britta McKenna
June 25, 2016

A note to give you an update on the past week and what's just ahead. The week following chemo is always challenging and this one was no exception. Maureen's white counts got out of whack, first up to 16 on Monday, then down to .6 two days later. She has been going in for shots to boost her counts and has been fatigued most of the week. The best, happiest booster is that Riley has been at home this past week and his craziness brings lots of joy that only a dog can give.

Coming up on Monday is a trip to her shoulder doctor at the University of Chicago. Prayers are needed for non-surgical options. You may remember that Maureen's journey started with pain in her shoulder that she thought was a torn rotator cuff. Her shoulder does not hurt nearly as much as it did in January, which is a the positive on which to focus. Maureen has scheduled her PET scan for mid-July, after her final round of chemo, which is the week of July 4-8. And so, the resting, and waiting, and worrying continues.

The flowers planted by the Garden Angels are just gorgeous, which doesn't surprise me at all with the amount of love and effort that went into planting them 4 weeks ago. We will need to call on the angels again in the future—I'll let you know when. It may just have to also include a pool party. There are only five Meal Train dates left to help the family get through treatment; if you can make a meal for the family, please sign up at Maureen's site.

Enjoy summer, I'm hoping you are making the time to soak in it.

Britta

SOME GOOD NEWS TO SHARE

Journal Entry by Maureen O'Brien

June 30, 2016

As I face my final round of chemo next Monday (which is good news in and of itself), I thought I would share with you some good news that happened this week. As many of you know, this all started with my inability to lift my left arm, and my belief that I had a torn rotator cuff. Turned out not to be so. Early on, it looked very much like I would have to have surgery on my left shoulder when the chemo was done. The disease had eaten away at the bone causing it to be unstable, much like my hip that needed a rod to stabilize it. We hoped that perhaps my shoulder could heal on its own. It was unlikely but it WAS possible.

Dan and I made the long trek to the University of Chicago Hospital to meet with Dr. Hue Luu, Associate Professor of Orthopedic Surgery and Associate Director, Molecular Oncology Lab. No doctors in the Fox Valley would touch my shoulder, but Dr. Petrucci, the guy that put the rod in my hip, recommended Dr. Luu. We took the X-ray that we had done in May for the doctor to review. When Dr. Luu put it up, it showed a fracture. Oh my God you've got to be kidding me. I started to panic. Dr. Luu suggested that we take some new X-rays since the ones we were viewing were almost a month old.

I got sent to the X-ray department where I was escorted to the changing room to put on one of those lovely, flowing hospital gowns! I started shaking as I changed my clothes. When I got into the Xray room, I just started to sob uncontrollably. I'm so tired of all of this. I so want this to be behind me! The Xray techs had no idea what was happening. They thought they were hurting me. Had it not been such a lousy circumstance, it might've been funny. Okay, probably some day it will be funny. But not today.

Dr. Luu wanted the whole enchilada. He instructed that I have photos taken of my hip, my right shoulder, and finally my left . . . a total of 14 X-rays. The sobbing continued. When the X-rays were complete, I was invited back to the changing room where I could become less of a patient and more of a person in my own clothes.

Back in Dr. Luu's office we reviewed the photos. "Your hip looks great and so does your right shoulder. Both are stable." Then he pulled up the X-ray of my left shoulder.

"Well, look at this," he beamed. "There is bone filling in here on its own. Since you're not having pain or discomfort, I think your body is trying to heal on its own. I don't think you'll need surgery. Come back and see me in October and we'll confirm."

The ability to exhale. Feels like the first time in a long time. Not facing surgery this fall feels like such a gift, and I am truly grateful. Knowing that my body is doing everything it can to heal on its own makes me so incredibly glad. Thank you, God!

Thanks for your continued prayers, meals, cards, and support along the way. I'll not ever be able to find the words of gratitude. I do hope you know.

As I face this final round of chemo, I'm both delighted and scared because I know that this is the time to eliminate this disease. On July 18 (Dan's birthday) I'll have my final PET Scan. I beg your prayers at 9 a.m. on that day. The scan absolutely must be clear. Please visualize that. I know that I still have work to do here in earth school! Praying that God thinks so too!

CHAPTER 20

KATHY GARRITY

DEAR FRIEND, TWO-TIME CANCER SURVIVOR

Kath and I have been neighbors and friends for over thirty-five years. We have shared a lot. Sharing a cancer diagnosis was not something either of us anticipated. When Kathy had breast cancer many years ago, I tried to be by her side and stand with her in her journey. The same year that I was diagnosed with lymphoma, she was again diagnosed with cancer, this time ovarian. We were in the same hospital, in the same room, at the same time, one floor apart. I remember praying fervently that my friend would survive, and she remembers praying the same for me. By the grace of God, we're both still here.

*Kathy's writing will help you remember to **"focus on things worth living for."** Sage advice at any time! Kath is one of the most positive people I know. I believe it's why she's beaten cancer so many times. Don't wait to get a potentially fatal diagnosis to start living. Live now!*

As I write, here I sit today at infusion. I only needed four grams of magnesium. This is how I spend my Wednesday mornings. The key words are "here I sit." For that, I am blessed!

I am a five-year survivor of ovarian cancer and a seventeen-year survivor of breast cancer. I am also so thankful and honored to be able to tell *my* story and to tell you, the reader, that your attitude and mindset will play such an important part in *your* story.

When Mo asked me to write, I was honored and a bit nervous. I accepted the task knowing that it might help someone else. My friendship with Mo goes way back, more than thirty-five years. As neighbors and very dear friends, we have laughed together, cried together, raised our children together, and experienced a zillion memorable moments together. We have shared so many things. We even shared a cancer diagnosis together!

I won't bore you with all the details of my treatment or what feels like a never-ending journey. However, it has been just that: quite the unique journey. Your journey will also be unique. I'd encourage you not to compare your journey with any other. That type of strategy isn't good for one's mindset. You are unique; your circumstances are unique. That's who your treatment must be planned for . . . you and only you! My hope is that you will find "glimmers of hope" and a few tangible ideas by reading stories like these.

I am an educated person, and I am a firm believer in *not* believing everything I read on the internet. During my journey, I stayed away from personal blogs. I only researched reputable websites (WebMD, the American Cancer Society, etc.). I never spent time researching my cancer fully, since I didn't want to read doom and gloom or focus on statistics. I was and am on *my own journey.* The one thing I truly believed was that I was *not* going to allow myself to die! I took one day at a time, dealt with that day, and said a thank-you prayer when the day was done. I still do.

> I TOOK ONE DAY AT A TIME, DEALT WITH THAT DAY, AND SAID A THANK-YOU PRAYER WHEN THE DAY WAS DONE. I STILL DO.

My family was and is wonderful. It was and is so tough on my family. I believe my husband, Ron, saved my life. He was with me 24/7, every step of the way. My adult daughter and son were ready at my beck and call: packing and changing wounds, caring for my ileostomy bag, walking me to the bathroom, and standing by to hold me up when my blood pressure dropped (or I did). My husband and son were experts at picking me up off the ground. Those were just a few of the "jobs" my family took on without hesitation. They became wound care specialists, ileostomy experts, personal chefs, and counselors, all within a moment's notice. Our belief was and still is that we can get through life's challenges, and any circumstance that arises because we are and will always be there for each other. They certainly were there for me for over nine months of treatment!

There was a bit of research that especially held true during my journey. The act of touch is very important for humans. Holding a hand, rubbing a forehead, or messaging a neck or shoulders is very soothing when a person is lying in a hospital bed. I know this from my education and my personal experience. During my stay in the ICU, my daughter would rub my head, hand, or arm, and the heart monitor would register a slower heartbeat indicating a more relaxed state. The doctors remarked how amazing this was. I know it aided with my recovery. High anxiety does not help one with recovery.

Friends took on the role of visiting periodically, making meals, or procuring meal services. They also checked in with my family to see if they needed breaks or groceries. They offered to sit with me during chemo. They would ask my family what was needed, since my family knew my day-to-day situation. There were times when, due to the chemo causing neuropathy, I could not move my fingers to text, so my daughter would have to do it for me. She became the best texter in our town! Letting everyone know my status regularly was important to my many friends, and she took charge of that task. Even if family didn't ask, friends took it upon themselves to provide whatever they could in terms of support. They did not ask; they just did. As part of someone's community of care, don't ask what you can do; just do it!

As a patient, it's great to have someone with you when you are getting chemo. Have deep or silly conversations, whichever feels right, but invite someone along. Even if you fall asleep, when you open your eyes, you'll realize how very reassuring it is to have someone with you. For the person with you, there is a feeling of satisfaction that they are helping you in some way. That creates a win-win situation!

As a support person, be proactive instead of reactive. It makes an unbelievable impression and is truly appreciated by the family and person with cancer. Ask about the family's favorite food and make that. Drop off a gift card to a grocery store, or better yet, do the shopping for them. It will be one of the greatest gifts you can give.

> AS A PATIENT, IT'S GREAT TO HAVE
> SOMEONE WITH YOU WHEN YOU ARE
> GETTING CHEMO. HAVE DEEP OR SILLY
> CONVERSATIONS, WHICHEVER FEELS
> RIGHT, BUT INVITE SOMEONE ALONG.

As I shared previously, Mo and I had cancer at the same time. I remember being in a wheelchair when my husband pushed me into Mo's hospital room. At that time, it was all I could do for my friend! Here we were, both fighting cancer, promising each other that there was no way we would let this monster get the best of us. Besides, how could our neighborhood function without us? We are the matriarchs of the neighborhood! We would get through this because we knew we just could and would not leave our families, friends, and homes. They needed us. I believed that I would make it through! Through your journey, you will need many people. You must believe that they need you too.

During that time, there were many days that I was so worried about Mo I didn't even think about myself or my own situation. I know she had the same thoughts about me! I suspect we actually helped each other get through the many months of treatments and numerous ups and downs simply by fighting our own battles.

ILLUMINATIONS

First, let's get to the tough question: "How am I supposed to get through this?" Or, if you're part of the community of care: "How do I support my friend or family member with cancer?"

My first bit of advice, from a voice of experience: *believe* that you will get through it. Just don't think (and say), "I am going to kick cancer's ass!" Believe me when I tell you there will be times that cancer will kick *your* ass. But if you truly believe and have a positive mindset, I believe you will get through it and ultimately have your own story to tell. Focus on something you want to live for. Don't focus on what brings you down. My constant thoughts were in anticipation of the arrival of my twin grandchildren. Now, my focus is on doing whatever I need to do to watch them grow up.

A close support group is vital. You need a community of care. You may be surprised at who your community will include! They might be family, close friends, or others you don't even know yet. You will draw strength from people you talk with, information you read, and, most importantly, from within yourself.

My second bit of advice: try with everything that you have to think *logically* and not just *emotionally* about your situation. Emotions can play havoc with your mindset and make you "crazy!"

I always wanted to be told the truth by my doctor and family members. When I needed explanations or questions answered, I would ask my doctor or nurses. I would not get my answer from the internet or health blogs or compare my story with another. I was, with the aid of my daughter, a strong advocate for myself. It's incredibly important to have an advocate with you when meeting with any health professionals. Always ask questions! I trusted my medical team, *and* there were times when we would ask for clarification on treatment or care. If something doesn't seem right to you, go with your gut. Be your own strongest advocate!

Third advice tip: always remember that it is OK to cry. You must also remember to laugh. My husband makes me laugh every day. It's medicine for the soul! To this day, I joke about my many "cancer perks": lost weight, new haircut and color, and not having to shave my legs. The list goes on . . .

Am I glad I had cancer? *Definitely not!* I don't take my situation lightly; I know that ovarian cancer likes to recur. But I am committed to believing in myself, the knowledge of my doctors, and the ability of my family and friends. This is my life, and I will *live* it.

So will you!

INDEPENDENCE WEEK BEGINS

Journal Entry by Britta McKenna

July 4, 2016

Mo checked into the hospital this morning for Knock Out, Round 6 chemo, and is well underway. Mo and Dan opened the door to her hospital room to find it decorated and filled with all of her nurses and medical staff to surprise her. Cake, flowers, cards, banner, even a note signed by Dr. Bayer who had not been Mo's oncologist since Round 3. Mo sported blinking patriotic glasses with a matching antenna. Yes, she's ending this final round with a bang. My husband Steve and I brought a 4th of July picnic, complete with brats, potato salad, deviled eggs, fruit salad and baked beans. The final celebratory treat . . . Grammie's blueberry pie! Checking out this Friday, and hoping to turn the page. Happy 4th to all!

JULY 5: KNOCKOUT ROUND

Journal Entry by Maureen O'Brien

July 5, 2016

Last night was awful. Lizzy spent the night. We got absolutely no sleep. The IV machine beeped at

12:30 a.m.

2:58 a.m.

3:29 a.m.

6:10 a.m.

6:39 a.m.

This means that a nurse must come and tap the air bubbles out of the line until the beeping stops. Yeh, sleep is overrated.

Today has been a relatively easy day, although I did have to have an echocardiogram which is scary. Doesn't hurt at all. It's an ultrasound used because chemo can sometimes damage the heart. I'm obviously hoping this is not one of those times!

Because I'm on a ridiculous amount of prednisone, I've gained seven pounds in one day which means Lasix is my newly added drug. It makes you urinate about every 10 minutes. OK, maybe that's a slight exaggeration. It does mean you spend a lot of your day in the bathroom.

I'm still hoping to get outside today which Alison, my nurse, promises will happen. Alison is like my own Snow White. She is beautiful, kind, and she was the catalyst for the decorating of my room, making the banner which everyone who has taken care of me—including my doctors signed, flowers, a signed card, and baking of the fabulous "Congratulations MO" cake. What an incredible heart!

Vernita, the woman responsible for the cleanliness of my room, came to see me today. Every time I am here, she comes and holds my hand, prays with me, and prays over me. Another reminder of the angels on earth.

So almost two days down and three to go. I think I can . . . I think I can . . . I think I can . . .

CHAPTER 21

ANNE "CECE" RODI

FRIEND, SORORITY SISTER

I know her as Cece. Her maiden name (and how I knew her in college) was Cecilia Cecilia. Her parents thought it was clever. As with most things, her name did not faze her.

*Cece was the gatherer of my other sorority sisters in Pittsburgh, who were desperate to understand how I was doing. She led them in **"sending symbols of love"** on a regular basis so that I would know they were with me on the journey. I did know. And I am so grateful.*

It was February 23, 2016. I was attending a Boy Scout Religious Service because at the time, I was employed by the Boy Scouts. Sitting in the church, my phone was vibrating. I saw it was a call from Maureen's cell phone. I decided I would catch it later, but then it rang again. I thought maybe Maureen's mom had passed away since she was battling dementia in a nursing home. I left the church and dialed her number. To my surprise, Maureen's husband Dan answered. He gave me the unbelievable news that Maureen had been diagnosed with non-Hodgkin's lymphoma and was very ill. He asked if I would call our other sorority sisters and let them know the situation. More particularly, he asked if they would please pray. I assured him I would.

I hung up the phone, still in shock. Making the calls to our sorority sisters, I finally realized the gravity of the words that were coming from my mouth. I was sobbing and shaking with fear. How could it be that this was happening? Was it possible that we might lose her? Maureen was so full of life. She was planting new ideas all the time. She was enjoying her growing family. She had raised four incredible kids. It was her turn to take it easy now. It wasn't supposed to happen like this. We were planning how we would spend our days together years from now creating chaos in nursing homes. Oh, how we would laugh. This could not be happening. Not like this. Not now.

Later that week, Dan called back to inform me that Maureen's chemo treatment was going to be expedited. Maureen was declining rapidly, and they could not wait. I tried to comfort Dan, knowing that no words would soothe the pain he was feeling. I felt helpless, but I knew I had to do something. I planned a luncheon to gather and update our sorority sisters, who were loving and praying for Maureen from a long distance.

I FELT HELPLESS, BUT I KNEW I HAD TO DO SOMETHING.

At lunch, feeling the magnitude of the miles between us and Maureen, we decided that we would all pitch in and send a basket of love—something from each of us—so she would know she was not alone on this journey. Frankly, this helped us as much as it helped Maureen and her family. Following that luncheon, we continued to meet regularly at luncheons to keep updated about Maureen's condition. I would call Dan every Sunday. Sometimes those calls were grueling. The news was not good, but we were committed to constant prayer.

I asked if he wanted me to come out, to drive from Pittsburgh to Chicago, just to be there. This was as much for me as for Maureen and her family. Dan did not immediately respond. I could tell he was lost in fear and grief, but Dan is a faith-filled man, and he let me know that he was trusting God.

A day later (now Holy Saturday), I learned from Dan that Maureen was in critical condition in the hospital. She had a fever. I called the sorority phone tree and asked that they pray hard. When I finished the calls, I hung up the phone and looked at my husband, Paul. Bursting into tears, I said, "I'm losing her." Paul tried to comfort me. He couldn't believe what he was hearing.

That afternoon, Britta McKenna posted through the CaringBridge site that only family was permitted in the hospital room. Tears streaming down my face, I asked God to help me. I looked down at a bag on the basement floor and saw a Divine Mercy pamphlet sticking out of it. I sat in my laundry room and began saying the chaplet. A very strange feeling came over me as I concentrated on the picture of Christ and the prayers I was saying and pictured the hospital bed that held Maureen. It was the closest I had felt to God in a long time.

As I finished my prayers, I shook myself and realized the phone was ringing. It was Dan saying the fever had broken. She was coming back to us! I realized I did not know where I'd gotten that Divine Mercy prayer pamphlet. I had not attended a spiritual retreat recently. How did it get in my bag? How was it in my basement? I believe God intervened when I asked for help. I was absolutely at my lowest point, but God was there.

Months went by, and we continued to have our sorority sister lunches. This was light that came from the darkness. So many of us had lost touch and now were reconnected. We continued to send symbols of love to Maureen, even though she was unable to speak to us and too sick to realize what we were sending. That was not the point. We knew that somewhere deep within her, she would know we were with her. Distance could not separate our hearts.

The treatments went on for months, from March to July. They included checking into the hospital and being connected to a twenty-four-hour chemo drip for a week at a time. She did that six times, with a two-week break between hospital stays.

The last chemo treatment started on July 4. We knew that this date represented something important for Maureen: it was her independence from this horrible disease! When she entered the hospital that day and the transporter escorted her and Dan to her room, they found the door was closed. This was odd. After the transporter knocked and got no answer, he gently and slowly opened the door.

Sounds of congratulations and cheering erupted. The nurses and staff that had taken care of Maureen for those six long weeks were waiting there in the hospital room to celebrate. It. Was. Almost. Over. The last round. They had cake, banners, cards, flowers . . . and tears.

On the late afternoon of July 8, the last day of treatment, when the last drop of chemo entered Maureen's body, loud sounds, music, and cheering made their way toward her hospital room. Friends, family, nurses, hospital staff, all adorned in celebratory hats, beads, and party clothes, marched into her room to the *Rocky* theme song, ready to parade her out of the hospital. It had been a long, arduous journey, and now it was over.

On July 18, we held our collective breath as Maureen had her final PET scan to see if the treatment had done its job. On July 20, we learned that it did!

To this day, I still have the voicemail message Maureen left on July 20, 2016, at 4:14 p.m., telling me that the treatment had worked. She. Was. Cancer. Free. I dropped to my knees in thanksgiving for God getting her through this horrible time. I decided I needed to see her. I would drive to Chicago. Now. Right now. I mapped out how to get there as quickly as possible. I was in a whirlwind comparing airlines, train schedules . . . I finally decided to just get in the car and drive. My son encouraged me, knowing that this drive was well beyond my comfort zone.

I HAD PRAYED SO HARD FOR
TOTAL RECOVERY. NOW IT WAS TIME
TO CELEBRATE.

I was very nervous about making this trip on my own, but I was determined to make good on my promise to Maureen to see her as soon as her treatment was finished and she was able to have visitors. I had prayed so hard for total recovery. Now it was time to celebrate.

I hit the highway at five in the morning on July 21. I thought back to when Maureen and I had met, all the antics of college life, and how much we took for granted. I thought about the previous July 4, 2015. I was visiting the O'Briens, and I started to have chest pain. Maureen rushed me to the hospital in her car. I was having a full-blown anxiety attack. She was so incredibly kind to sit with me for four hours and give me comfort. I apologized for ruining the family's Fourth of July, and I promised that if there were ever a time that I could return the favor, I would. We laughed, knowing that would never happen. Yet here we were, exactly one year later, and I was fulfilling that promise.

As I drove, I considered all these things: how fragile life is, how much we take for granted. I wondered what I might say when I saw Maureen. How would she look? Would she be able to hug me? I remember feeling so nervous.

I finally pulled into the driveway. Maureen opened the door, and the love poured out.

ILLUMINATIONS

If I could recommend anything, it would be this: *Be present.*

Do something. The "what" doesn't matter. If you are a distance away, send cards, surprises, emails, or flowers. You can send a lawn service, a cleaning service, or a snow removal service—and not just once. Lots of people are present at the start of this journey, but focus wanes. For the person going through it, the journey is long. Stay on the journey with them.

Send notes through CaringBridge (or whatever communication platform is available). These messages can always be read aloud to the patient, even if they are not capable of reading them themselves.

Don't forget to support the family. They are carrying a lot. Love them. Hold them up. Be present for them.

If you are reading this, know that you are loved and held in prayer by our community of care, Maureen's community. You are not alone. We are all here to love and support each other, and it is our intention to do just that.

AND THEN THERE WERE NONE

Journal Entry by Britta McKenna

July 8, 2016

When there is a bag delay switching out to the final 30 minutes of drip, the surprise party waiting in the lobby abandons the plan and storms room 2660. Dancing to the theme music from "Rocky," the first wave of well-wishers surprised Mo and as tears of joy were wiped away, the reality of the last day of the last round set in. Yes, chemo is complete, and Mo is on the other side of the treatment, and home resting with family.

Thank you all for being part of the O'Brien support team. The power of prayer, home-cooked meals, massage, cards, visits, garden Angels and gift givers have fueled Mo over the past 5 months.

God bless you all along the way.

Britta

TEST ON MONDAY

Journal Entry by Maureen O'Brien

July 15, 2016

Monday, July 18, is the big day. It's Dan's birthday, and at 9 a.m., I'll have my PET Scan. Of course, I'm scared. AND . . . I want to know.

This week held a mixed bag of emotions for me. My sister Karen calls it a release. I was calling it a meltdown. I've cried a lot, laughed some, and have gone deeper into myself than I ever have before. I've had physical limitations besides those which are usual and obvious. I lost control of my bowels while at my office. Probably more than you need to know. I was horrified, angry, embarrassed, and thanked God for my assistant, Nicole, who never gets rocked by any of the stuff that happens, over which I have no control. There is so little dignity with this disease.

I've had many moments of being mad at God, not understanding why this had to be. I don't want to be mad at God. I've gotten through the worst (I think) with the HELP of God. It seems as though looking forward is where my sights ought to be focused, being grateful that I've gotten to this moment. And yet . . .

I attended the healing service this week at my church. I prayed fervently for some sign that God was in the middle of this;

that I would be OK. Later that evening, Dan and I went to watch the sunset. A song came on the radio which I had not ever heard before by Danny Gokey. It's called, "Tell Your Heart to Beat Again." I *knew* the song was directed specifically at me. It was my sign! Take a listen https://www.youtube.com/watch?v=azYK8I2uoog

Mariann Schira came over this week and sprayed our rod iron furniture. Bright and cheery. Lime green—which also is the color of lymphoma. It's beautiful! Today as I write, I am breathing in the beauty of my backyard and the oasis that the hands of the Garden Angels created for me. Breathing is really the only thing I have control over. I continue to breathe.

Thanks in advance for your storming of heaven on my behalf between now and Monday. I have so appreciated all that you've done for me; the prayers, the meals, thetflowers, the cards, the emails, the visits, the words of encouragement, the parade out of the hospital :). I especially appreciated seeing my 6'5" brother Bill, and his wife Kathy, who flew in from Pittsburgh for the parade, in a lime green plastic top hat marching in the line. Not Bill's regular mojo. Complete surprise. I did not know they were coming or that any of this was going to happen. Touched my soul. Seeing my sister Karen in her Iron Woman suit was also pretty great, and the facetime *"Live from Kentucky Talent Show,"* provided by my sister Patricia's grandkids Will, Claire, and Elizabeth was terrific. Later, I'm going to write about having a friend like Britta McKenna in my life. That'll be an entire essay in and of itself. What a gift.

All of YOU have inspired me to keep putting one foot in front of the other. Know you have made a difference in this long, arduous journey. Looking forward to doing a victory lap with you on Wednesday, July 20, at 1:20 when we get the results of the PET SCAN. You are love in action. I am grateful.

CALLING ALL PRAYER WARRIORS

Journal Entry by Britta McKenna

July 16, 2016

Hello Friends of Mo,

Mariann Schira contacted me this week with an idea to organize prayer for Maureen this weekend and in the 9:00 hour on Monday. So, as easy as it is for me to make a post, we are asking you to send a prayer storm to surround Mo this weekend in whatever way you pray or wherever you worship—be it in church, synagogue, prayer group or by communing with nature. Lift up Maureen, Dan and the O'Brien family and pray for a clear PET scan and pray for her strength to be calm with the waiting and quell the storm of anticipation.

If you are able to join Mariann Schira on Monday at Holy Cross Church in the Adoration Chapel at 9:00 a.m. to 10:00 a.m., please do so. Enveloping Mo and Dan and family with prayer is the best medicine right now.

Pray On!

Britta (on behalf of Mariann)

PART

5

HEALTH CARE

AS POINTS OF LIGHT

If you look up "health care" in Webster's dictionary, you will read this: *"the organized provision of medical care to individuals or a community."*

My interpretation of that can be summed up in a single word: *proficiency*. That was also my expectation. I expected these people to be proficient at their profession. What I did not expect was the level of care that I received, not only for my physical well-being but for my emotional, spiritual, and mental well-being as well. I had angels in scrubs!

I'm not sure I can accurately describe this heart-centered, love-inducing care with words. It goes beyond words. What I know for sure is that these people absolutely carried me when I was unable to carry myself. They advocated for me. They cheered for me. They cried with me. They laughed with me. They trusted that I could, that I *would* get through the treatment and come back to health. It was easier to believe because *they believed.*

On the first day of the last round of my treatment, they surprised me with a celebration of banners, flowers, cards, and gifts. The cards were signed by every health-care professional who had cared for me in those thirty days of chemo. They cheered and cried tears of joy. On the last day of my treatment, when the final chemo bag dripped its last drop, they led a parade out of the hospital. When I got to the final doors, Katie, one of my favorite nurses, leaned down to my wheelchair and whispered, "Never look back." She convinced me that I was done with cancer and that I only had good things to which I could look forward.

It is impossible not to look back. But when I do look back, I recognize the extraordinary care I had that enabled me to look forward! Of course, I am forever grateful.

CHAPTER 22

SONALI M. SMITH, MD, CHIEF OF HEMATOLOGY/ ONCOLOGY, UNIVERSITY OF CHICAGO MEDICINE

ELWOOD V. JENSEN PROFESSOR OF MEDICINE; CO-LEADER, CANCER SERVICE LINE; DIRECTOR, LYMPHOMA PROGRAM, UNIVERSITY OF CHICAGO; MAUREEN'S LEAD ONCOLOGIST

Dr. Smith has recently become the Chief of Hematology/Oncology for the University of Chicago Hospitals. Originally, Dr. Smith was my "second opinion." My sister Patricia insisted that we get another opinion. It was Dr. Smith's protocol that was followed and executed at our local hospital. Imagine, doctors from two separate hospital systems willing to work together to get me well. Dr. Smith is now my number one opinion!

*Her ability to articulate that **"what paves the road is instinct, knowledge, trust, and hope"** proved to be the exact right prescription for me to believe I could beat this disease. Her ability to combine that eighteen-inch vertical drop—the distance between head and heart—helped me to navigate forward, always forward. I know her words will do the same for you.*

There is a skill in medicine that cannot truly be taught. It is the ability to walk into a room and know, right away, who is sick and who is not. This skill is somewhat of a survival instinct. It helps frame the discussion; it helps the physician assist the family and the patient in knowing what lies ahead. It does not predict who lives or who dies, but it is a barometer that shapes all that comes next.

This is what was going through my mind when Maureen came to the clinic five years ago. She was in a wheelchair, her husband and sister hovering over her. She had a vibrant face reflecting years of being a mover and shaker and go-getter. But something had drained the color from her skin and detracted from the pretty lipstick she wore. She was trying so hard to be sharp, to be on top of the situation as she was in nearly every other aspect of her life. Yet the situation was on top. She knew this and was truly struggling. She could not shake my hand because the cancer had invaded the bones of her right arm. Her family took notes and tried to absorb all that she could not.

You see, Maureen had a very aggressive, very advanced form of diffuse large B-cell lymphoma. Diffuse large B-cell lymphoma is the most common form of lymphoma in the world, and it accounts for the highest number of lymphoma-related deaths worldwide. In many people, standard combination chemotherapy can cure the disease. Unfortunately, the standard of care does not work for everyone, and knowing who will be cured and who will not be cured lies at the heart of the challenge for an oncologist treating patients with this sneaky and nefarious disease.

For Maureen, the cancer had set up shop in innumerable sites, including her bones. She was physically weak, in pain, struggling to string together coherent questions and understand the answers. She had to let her family speak for her. It was clear that she was a very sharp and self-made woman and that letting others take over was foreign to her being. However, she also clearly trusted her husband and family, and that allowed our conversation to move forward in a productive way.

Sick. Definitely sick. My mind was racing as I walked into the room to see her looking so incredibly ill and yet feeling so hopeful that I would be the answer to her problems. She wanted to live. She had so much to live for. How to frame the discussion? Tell her that "cure" was the goal but that many people do not get to the goal? Or tell her that everything would be fine in order to give some hope? Try to ease her anxiety by saying that everything would be OK? Or provide realistic information that would let her know about the very tough road that lay ahead? Would this discourage and depress her?

> THIS INTERNAL STRUGGLE BETWEEN
> HOPE AND REALISM IS A REPEATED ONE
> FACED BY EVERY ONCOLOGIST.

To be honest, this internal struggle between hope and realism is a repeated one faced by every oncologist. Being human, an oncologist's own constitution will come through. I finished medical school in 1994 and have spent the majority of my career as an academic clinical oncologist dedicated to treating lymphoma. I joined the faculty at the University of Chicago in 2001, and lymphoma has been my primary area of focus. The fact that I am a hopeful optimist is not something I really knew about myself for many years. My patients made me realize this over time. I realized that I loved to give good news and provide hope. But there were also times when I felt that giving hope was wrong, just a false promise. It took years of experience and discussions with patient after patient after patient for me to realize that giving hope was always right, but it had to be tempered by the situation at hand. This is the art of medicine: being truthful and hopeful no matter how bleak the situation.

> THIS IS THE ART OF MEDICINE: BEING TRUTHFUL AND HOPEFUL NO MATTER HOW BLEAK THE SITUATION.

I walked into the room and moved the chair so that I could face Maureen and all of her family simultaneously and without having to shift back and forth. My main goal in patient care is to educate. Educate about the disease, about the prognosis, about the treatment. Education is powerful, and I always want my patients to feel that they have some degree of control over this disease. I discussed how diffuse large B-cell lymphoma is part of a complex family of blood cancers arising from cancerous B-cells. We discussed some of the biologic features of diffuse large B-cell lymphoma and how they affect the likelihood of a cure. Her biopsy confirmed the diagnosis, but there were some high-risk features that made standard chemotherapy less likely to succeed.

For one thing, she had a very high lactate dehydrogenase (LDH) that suggested how quickly the disease was growing. This high LDH put her in an unusual situation where treating the disease might put her at risk for tumor lysis syndrome—rapid tumor cell kill that would release toxins into her blood that could damage her kidneys and heart. She needed careful initiation of chemotherapy to protect her organs. The University of Chicago pathology review also confirmed that she had a variant of diffuse large B-cell lymphoma more properly called "high-grade B-cell lymphoma." This was a less well-described form of the disease, and it was becoming increasingly clear that the standard treatment would be insufficient. She also had a poor "performance status," a term used to predict who could or could not tolerate intensive treatment.

Sick. Tumor lysis. Wheelchair. Hope. Cure. Survival. Thrival (not a word, but it should be!). I pictured the trajectory of these words and channeled my positive, hopeful self. We discussed that the road would be hard and that standard chemotherapy would not be enough. She needed more intensive treatment than the standard of care, including directing chemotherapy into the fluid around the brain. But she was strong and had wonderful family support. One cannot underestimate the impact of family love and support. It is at the core of positive outlook and hope. The battle between disease biology and social determinants of outcome was on display. She had it all, and there was no reason not to give this every effort possible.

> ONE CANNOT UNDERESTIMATE THE IMPACT OF FAMILY LOVE AND SUPPORT. IT IS AT THE CORE OF POSITIVE OUTLOOK AND HOPE.

In the end, Maureen went through six rounds of more intensive chemotherapy than the standard of care. She had some tough times but started to steadily improve. Given the distance from her home to the University of Chicago, she was treated by a partnering oncologist. He and I spoke about her plan, her prognosis, and the details of treatment with the goal of "cure" in mind. I next met with Maureen after four rounds of chemotherapy and again after six rounds of treatment. *She walked in both times.* She had the same lipstick and makeup, but when I saw her after her sixth round of treatment, she had an inner glow because she was healing, and she was headed toward cure. I started to know the real Maureen.

Cure, in lymphoma, is defined by remission plus time. The first goal is to achieve remission, meaning that the cancer cannot be seen on a PET or CT scan. *Cure* is defined as being free of disease for at least five years. However, at least 40 to 50 percent of people with Maureen's high-risk-disease-related features will have the disease come back and therefore will not be cured.

Every time she would come to the clinic, we would count the months since remission and cheer that we were closer to cure. Every time, we would marvel at her transformation from a completely debilitated woman to someone who moved her company forward to empower other women to achieve their highest potential. As with so many other people I am privileged to meet, Maureen became a friend. Our conversations focused more and more on her career, on her work, on her passions. We spoke less and less about lymphoma, and it became an afterthought in our clinic visits.

Maureen will have hit her five-year anniversary of the end of treatment in the summer of 2021. So much has happened during this time in her life, in my life, and in the world at large. While I have no idea what lies on the road ahead, I know we will celebrate both externally with cheers and internally with gratitude that We. Are. Here. Onward!

ILLUMINATIONS

What paves the road: instinct, knowledge, trust, and hope.

DA BRIDE IS HOME! BY DAN O'BRIEN

Journal Entry by Maureen O'Brien

July 21, 2016

Da Bride is home. We are so grateful. Gratitude feels like thankfulness from 10,000 feet. It is a deep, far reaching feeling. It has a quiet peacefulness like the morning after a storm. Da Bride is home, we are so grateful.

Joy. There is a joy that is related to happiness. It has the wonderful sharp peaks of the pure energy of life. There is a grander joy that is rooted in gratitude. It is more massive and breathtaking. It is widespread and fills all of the nooks and crannies in life. It is on a continental scale as when the land appeared from the sea. Da Bride is home, and we are filled with both flavors of joy . . . and we are so grateful.

Three days ago, Da Bride had a PET scan after 6 rounds of chemotherapy. Yesterday, four family members were in the doctor's office to receive the results. Silence greeted the doctor's message that no signs of cancer remained, then a clamor ensued to make sure that we had understood the words correctly. As the turmoil subsided a bit, we all became aware of Da Bride's sobs.

Deep racking, huge, body shaking sobs. Quick inhales, long, deep exhales. There were tears, but the power in the room was in the large sobs as Da Bride drank in the long awaited and much prayed for news. A jet engine makes noise, but the power is in the exhaust. With each sob, tension and pressure left her body while relief rushed in with quick gulps of air. No one in the room had understood the intense stress and pressure Da Bride was subjected to while leading up to that meeting. Some of it had been gathered during the long trek through six rounds of chemo. Much of it had accumulated after the sixth round waiting for the PET scan, enduring the need to be still and deal with claustrophobia during the test, and then waiting into the third day for the results.

People waiting for critical news live in a stress unknown by the rest of us.

We know many people have prayed for us and we are thankful. We are awed by the power of prayer. We watched the breath of life inhaled by the creature who, unable to hold it, released it with all the tensions of the moment, only to reach for more. More was available, much more. It was like drinking from a fire hose.

We are awed by the power of prayer. If we will have the breath of life, we need to breathe it out. If we will have love, we need to breathe it out also. We have felt the outpouring of love from all of you. We have felt prayed for by many, many people.

We feel the need to ask all of those who said a prayer for us to return and say more prayers of thanksgiving for favors granted in His mercy. We want to walk with the leper who returned to give thanks after he was cured. Please say a prayer of thanksgiving. Please.

Da Bride is home, we are so grateful.

Blessed be God in his angels and in his saints.

Dan

CHAPTER 23

JULIE BROWN, ONCOLOGY NURSE

> *Julie Brown is the kind of professional that you hope you encounter in a health crisis. She has a magnetic smile and laugh, and her kindness enters the room before she does. Julie's account of **"joining the support team"**—my team—confirms the importance of the advocacy of nurses as part of your health squad in your community of care!*

As a nurse on an inpatient hospital oncology unit, rarely a day goes by that I don't see someone at some stage of their cancer journey. From the day of the diagnosis to the end of their journey and everywhere in between, I see it all. It is often a very emotion-filled time for patients and families trying to digest and navigate through the ups and downs of it all.

And then we have the patients who come in for their planned chemo treatments and need to remain in the hospital setting due to their regimen, which is usually several days. Trying to remember five years ago can be daunting, as so many things and events blend and become a little fuzzy, but there are certain things that are still so very clear and vivid that I will never forget about the time with Maureen O'Brien.

I remember feeling a little anxious and stressed the morning of her admission. I wasn't even the nurse assigned to her that day, but I knew how very sick she was. I always try to pause and say a little prayer for the patient and their family. I know it must be a scary and extremely difficult time for them. As my coworkers went in and out of her room that day, I could sense the urgency as they cared for her. I was hoping beyond hope that things were going to be OK.

After the initial treatments were underway and Maureen had started to come in for her scheduled cycles, it became clear that this was a special and in-control kind of woman. I could tell by her support—the entourage of her family, friends, and faith community—that she was on her way and was determined to beat this cancer! She always had a smile on her face and her makeup just right, and her room was filled with positive energy and uplifting pictures and cards. Her husband Dan was by her side every step of the way. This was no easy journey by any stretch, but Maureen had a way of making it look like a cakewalk. Well . . . maybe not really a cakewalk.

AS A NURSE, YOU BECOME INVESTED IN THE JOURNEY OF YOUR PATIENT. YOU WANT SO BADLY FOR ALL OF THIS TO BE WORTH IT FOR EVERYONE INVOLVED.

Having a week at a time, cycle after cycle, to get to know your patient can be a good thing or a not-so-good thing. In Maureen's case, it was a good thing. As a nurse, you become invested in the journey of your patient. You want so badly for all of this to be worth it for everyone involved. Seeing her progress and improvement over the weeks and months gave me hope. I wanted so much for her to beat this.

We celebrated with Maureen as she arrived the morning of her last cycle. We had planned this with her family so we could make it a surprise. She *was* surprised! Several of us were in her room waiting for her arrival with balloons, streamers, banners, and cupcakes. We tried our best to be quiet, and when she came through the door and saw us, she was in tears. So were we. Tears of joy and thankfulness flowed. She had made it this far after a very rocky start.

For me, this is always the best part: celebrating the *end* of the treatment journey while hoping and praying it really *is* the end. Once our patients have completed their treatments, we send them on their way. Often, we don't know what happens to them down the road. But Maureen kept us informed. She would drop by to let us know how her follow-up visits went and thank us for being a part of her being alive and thriving. This means the world to a nurse who has been part of the journey.

ILLUMINATIONS

If you're a nurse, encouraging your patient and their support system is key. Your patient needs a support system. Help them to create a plan of support, and help them to understand that it's OK to ask for help. Going through cancer is tough, but going through it alone is the worst. Help them understand that having someone by their side makes the journey just a little more tolerable.

ONE MONTH OUT— RECOGNIZING GOODNESS

Journal Entry by Maureen O'Brien

August 8, 2016

It was one month ago today that I was part of the greatest parade...the parade OUT of the hospital signifying my last round of
chemo! Remembering that parade still makes me smile.

In the days since, I have had strong days and weak days. The
weak days make me crazy. Tears flow. I can't name the reason. I'm
slow in my movements. That frustrates me. I fatigue easily. I want
to push through it. I think I should be farther along. It just is. Then, I
try to focus on the goodness—all of the people who have held me
up for the last six months. You, who are reading this! I think about
the things I have learned. Family matters. Forgiveness matters.
People matter. Life matters. Cancer sucks.

As I think about the goodness that emerged in the middle of
this darkness, I realize that there were so many "here on earth angels" who stood with and continue to stand with me, beyond what
I ever could've imagined. One of those angels is Britta McKenna.

When you look up the word *goodness* in the dictionary, you'll
see ***Britta's picture***. If I tried for the rest of my lifetime, I could not

reciprocate the goodness that Britta has shown me on this journey. From arranging the meal train, organizing the Garden Angels (which still takes my breath away), visits, thank yous on an excel spread sheet, keeping Riley, to staying overnight in the hospital with me, Britta offered a kind of hope and strength that I could lean on when I could not find my own way. She is a leader. An organizer. A take control kind of person. Exactly what you need when your life feels *out* of control.

Light and darkness cannot share the same space at the same time. Britta brings light. She illuminates. It is who she is and what she does. She has a knowingness about what needs to be done. She doesn't ask permission. She just does it.

There is so much that all of us can learn from Britta. Extension of self. Action. Looking for ways to use her life to help others. I'm not sure how we would've kept putting one foot in front of the other without her. She is amazingly strong. Focused. Tenacious. Diligent. I'd invite each of us, all of us, to take a look at the places in our own lives where we have the opportunity to create goodness in the life of another, and then "Britta Up!" Do it! Not tomorrow, today! Imagine the goodness we could create in the world!

Britta, you are loved beyond words. Thanks for being "goodness" in my life!

GARDEN ANGELS GATHERING & POOL PARTY SEPTEMBER 10

Journal Entry by Britta McKenna
August 21, 2016

Calling all Garden Angels on Saturday, September 10th at 10 am. Mo's energy levels are slow to return and she needs a angel assist with yard work as the season winds down. We'll work at the O'Brien's weeding and working in the yard from 10-Noon, then share a picnic poolside together. Bring your favorite snack or picnic item to share and don't forget your swimsuit and towel too!

Comment on this thread if you are able and if you are able, come and join us. Feel free to come for the gardening or join us at Noon for the picnic and swimming portion. Mo looks forward to seeing everyone.

Where: O'Brien Home

What to bring: work/garden gloves, yard waste bag, loppers, hedge trimmers (electric), fertilizer (flower and shrub), swimsuit, towel, and snack/picnic side dish.

Contact Mariann for more information.

CHAPTER 24

KATIE KATHRO (LEMAIRE), ONCOLOGY NURSE

> *Katie was one of the first nurses that I encountered. She had a great impact not only on me but on my entire family. The care and grace with which she showered all of us was and is incredible to witness and receive. Katie felt like family. She listened. She laughed. She loved—all of us. Her message of **"cherishing the connection"** is real and relevant to this day. We all cherish our connection with Katie.*

Mo has got to be my most special patient. I've been a nurse for eleven years, ten of those years spent on the oncology floor. For me personally, the hardest part about caring for oncology patients isn't even death. The hardest is wondering how they are doing after they leave the hospital. So many patients come and go. Often, once they leave, I never get to see them again.

As a full-time nurse, on average, we care for about 21 patients a week. Now multiply that number by 52. That's almost 1,100 in one year. Just one year. You want to know how many come back to say hello or let us know how they are doing? In my ten-year career, there have been *two*. That's OK. I understand it. What patient wants to come back to a place that likely held nothing but bad memories? I probably wouldn't want to go back either.

> THE HARDEST PART ABOUT CARING FOR ONCOLOGY PATIENTS IS WONDERING HOW THEY ARE DOING AFTER THEY LEAVE THE HOSPITAL.

Mo is different. She has filled a hole for me. She has involved me in her life after the hospital. I guess you could say a nurse cares about a patient long after they leave, and in this special case, my patient was thinking about me too. Mo has visited the hospital staff multiple times over the years. I want to say she even came in on a holiday while we were working. *A holiday!* She has invited us to her home for lunch to just say thank you. She has spoken at several seminars to help impact women across the world and show her gratefulness.

There were a few days in caring for Mo that I specifically remember, even after all this time. One of them was when I met her sister Patricia. I was caring for Mo that day. I even remember the room number: 2638. What I most remember was that she was having a really rough day. She was tired, in pain, and really not feeling well. She had little to no energy. I felt like such a bad nurse that day. There was nothing I could do to make her feel better. It seemed we had tried everything. I remember she had an ice cap, ice booties, and iced hand mittens because she was trying to reduce her neuropathy symptoms that came with chemo.

The chemo treatment was so nasty, so hard on her body. I walked into the break room and just started crying with my charge nurse, Tina. I felt like Mo was slowly dying right in front of me. I could see the weight falling off her; she couldn't stand even to pivot to use the bathroom. She was scared, and so was I. I kept thinking that she was my mom's age. What would I do if this were my mom?

A nursing assistant came and found me in the break room and said that Mo's sister was there and that she wanted to see me. I had heard about Mo's sister, the nurse. And not just a nurse, but the Associate Dean of Nursing at the University of Kentucky. My heart was pounding. I didn't want her sister to see that I was doing a horrible job of keeping her sister comfortable. I didn't want her to worry. We would *keep trying*. I have three sisters of my own. They are my best friends, and I would go to the ends of the earth for them. I felt like I could feel the depths of her pain.

I wiped my tears and walked toward the room. Patricia was waiting for me outside in the hallway. I introduced myself, and she said, "I know who you are. I'm so grateful to meet you. I hear about Nurse Katie all the time." She asked me if there was anything that she could do to help.

This was not what I was expecting. Here we were, two professionals, struggling to help our patient and sister. We sat in the chairs outside the room for a little while. I reviewed meds we had tried, position changes, relaxation techniques, anything I could think of. Her sister thanked me, and when we both dried our tears, we went into the room together. Mo was crying, and then I was crying. Again. I sat on her bed for the longest time, and we just talked and cried. As I write this, I'm getting emotional.

I remember ending my shift that night. Mo asked if I would be in the next day to finish the round of chemo with her. I was not scheduled to work, but I promised I would handpick her nurse. Mo's face fell, and her eyes again filled with tears. I could see she was disappointed.

Later that night, at home, lying in my bed, I was thinking about what else I could do to help. I called work and asked to be put back on the next day's shift so that I could finish that treatment with Mo. I'll never forget her husband's smile and Mo's tears of relief when I walked in the next morning. "*Surprise!*" I said. "Let's do this!" Somehow, there was an energy in the room that day that hadn't been there the day before: a physical energy in Mo, a pep in my step, and a spiritual energy that was helping both of us in a way we both needed. Mo knew she was not doing this alone.

I hung that next bag and watched her go through the horrible body aches and chills. But she did it. She survived. With her husband, her sweet daughter, her sons, her sisters, and her sisters-in-law by her bedside, we celebrated that round being done.

I can't remember the number of times I cared for Mo. There were just too many to count. She impacted my life as a young nurse. I was going through some of my own personal difficulties at the time—a terrible divorce—and she allowed me to share my story with her. She gave me words of encouragement and reminded me to keep the faith.

Years went by, and she would stop by just to say hi or to tell us she had received a clean scan. In my eleven years as a nurse, only one other patient has ever done this. I think that for caregivers, hearing from patients after they leave the hospital helps us heal the wounds and wonderings within us rather than leaving them open to the unknown. Mo thinks I impacted her life. Really, we have impacted each other, and that is truly something beautiful. *Cancer-free!*

ILLUMINATIONS

As a caregiver, if there's something you can do that you know will make a difference to the patient, do it. Your positivity and care can make a huge difference in a patient's outlook and help them understand that they are not alone.

A SIGNIFICANT LOSS

Journal Entry by Maureen O'Brien

September 21, 2016

On Monday, my beautiful Mother, Helen Vernal, left this earthly home to join my Dad in heaven. Of course, I'm heartbroken. The gift of memories abounds for my siblings and me. Mom would be so proud of the strength of our bond.

When my Dad was dying, I asked him to send me a sign after he passed that he was OK. Shortly after he died, I saw a rainbow in the sky and knew it was from him. Monday, when Dan and I checked into the hotel in Wauwatosa, this is the first thing that we saw from our hotel room window. I think this is my Dad's way of letting me know that my Mom made it "home."

I love you Mom.

HELEN VERNAL,

MAUREEN'S MOM

Lower: Helen Vernal (Mom), Maureen
Upper: Patricia, Karen

*On September 19, three months after Maureen learned of her re-
mission, our beloved mother went to be with the angels. When we
arrived in Wisconsin for Mom's services, we saw the most beautiful
rainbow over the Cheesecake Factory. This was her favorite place.
She was letting us know that she was OK. She was home!*

*We believe that somehow, even with Alzheimer's, Mom knew
Maureen had made it, and she felt it was OK for her to go home to
join our dad in heaven. And still, we will never let go!*

CHAPTER 25

ALISON LUND, ONCOLOGY NURSE

I called her my very own Snow White. Alison looks like a Disney princess and has the demeanor to match. Kind. Loving. Sweet. Always a smile on her face. Alison lights up any space that she enters. She was the catalyst for the celebration of my last round of chemo. She is an incredible baker and would bring me treats during my chemo stays. I'm pretty sure that's not part of her job description, but Alison goes well beyond the job.

Alison is a master at **"giving hope"** when all seems hopeless. So many times, she'd give me a shout-out and cheer as I struggled to walk once around the 2600 floor with my walker while in chemo. She's the best cheerleader, advocate, and personal princess nurse any patient could ever hope to call their own.

I have been an oncology nurse since 2009. There are certain situations and patients that you will never forget as a nurse. Maureen O'Brien (MO) is one of those patients for me.

I remember the first time I heard about MO's situation. I was in awe of how swiftly things were happening regarding her diagnosis. For example, when cancer is suspected in a patient, the typical course of action is to obtain a bone marrow biopsy, wait for results, then begin treatment. It can take time to get everything scheduled and wait for results. I remember with MO, her oncologist wanted to expedite this process. I can only imagine that he felt she did not have time to wait.

MO initially presented to the hospital with a fractured bone in her shoulder as a result of her lymphoma. She also had to have a metal rod inserted next to her femur to secure the stability of that bone. Her oncologist worked diligently to coordinate multiple procedures that would happen at the same time as the surgery to insert the rod. During the same surgery, MO had a bone marrow biopsy obtained, lymph nodes removed, and an implanted port-a-cath placed. These would typically be three different procedures at three different times. But time was of the essence: her oncologist knew she needed the biopsy in order to stage the cancer, and she would need to have a port placed for intensive chemotherapy.

I was not MO's nurse at the time of her diagnosis. I was assigned to be her nurse after her first cycle of chemotherapy had begun. Because of the delay in being assigned as her nurse, I had a chance to observe from the outside. I remember seeing numerous family members going in and out of her room. When I was finally assigned to be her nurse, I recall being very intimidated, and I was nervous about caring for MO. She had an overwhelming amount of family members caring for her. But what I perceived as an intimidating situation was such a blessing. She had so many friends and family members who loved her and wanted her to receive the best care, just as her nursing and medical staff did. I quickly realized these friends and family members were on the same team as we, her caregivers, were. We all wanted to see MO come out on the other side and beat this cancer!

Once MO's first cycle of chemo was complete, she was able to be discharged home. The chemo regimen she was on required her to be admitted to the hospital for five days at a time every twenty-one days. She did this six times. To say MO and I got to know each other would be an understatement. Few patients are admitted to our unit for the duration and frequency that MO was, so naturally I got to know her very well. I requested to care for MO each time she came into the hospital, and I believe she enjoyed my being her nurse. I knew her chemo regimen backward and forward. I knew the little things that she preferred to make her chemotherapy cycle go smoothly. I felt like I was on her team of advocates, and I was honored to be in that position.

Toward the end of her chemo cycles, MO developed foot drop because of her treatments. She was having difficulty walking and was at risk of falling. I strongly advocated for her to receive a special foot brace to prevent her from being injured. Although there were barriers, MO was able to receive the treatment she needed.

I am so lucky to have met MO and been able to learn how to be a better nurse through caring for her. She frequently visited our nursing unit after she received good news to let us know that she was doing well. It is very fulfilling to be able to hear about your patients' successes. Inpatient oncology nurses frequently do not get the chance to celebrate victories with their patients.

I make it a point to celebrate every win with my patients, not just the big wins. There are some patients who do not get to have a big win or hear they are in remission, and I help patients celebrate whenever possible. Whether it is being able to eat a full meal, walk down the hallway of the hospital, finish their last cycle of chemo, or find out their cancer is in remission, celebrating landmarks with your patients can help revitalize their spirit and give them hope. Giving cancer patients hope can sometimes be exactly what they need. And it is my honor as a nurse to provide that for my patients.

ILLUMINATIONS

As a nurse, I strongly feel that we should behave as advocates for our patients. Every patient, not just the ones with whom we form a bond. There are patients who do not have the same support system that MO had. These patients need an advocate, too, probably even more so. I will always fight for what is right for my patients; that is what we must do as nurses.

CALLING ALL PRAYER WARRIORS—
ANXIOUS FOR MY NEXT TICKET!

Journal Entry by Maureen O'Brien
November 7, 2016

The last four months have been joy filled—no doctor appointments, no shots, blood work only once ... which looked fine. Eight of my sorority sisters drove out from Pittsburgh for a weekend and to attend the Danny Gokey concert. Pure joy and laughter. Prior to encountering cancer, I had no appreciation for the freedom I had in my own life. Part of my life's work now I believe is to help others trust that all we take for granted could be gone tomorrow. I thought I always knew this, lived it. A life threatening illness brings the reality of that message home.

There has been a really great progression forward. I remember writing about *longing for the mundane.* I have a brand-new appreciation for the mundane. I can drive my car. I can walk without assistance from another person or a walker, albeit not long distances. Fatigue lingers. I'm able to work. In fact, last week, I participated in our first Forum in eight months. I felt scared. Could I do it? Could I stand in front of others without breaking down? Did I have the strength to speak my new truth? Would I be willing to share? Could I show vulnerability and still be a leader?

273

The Forum was held in a beautiful space—the Gaylord Golf Resort in Nashville. Breathtakingly beautiful! Fog caressed the ground and was slowly rising as we made the winding ride to the clubhouse. I believe the fog was the universe whispering to me my first message for the day. "Fog will rise. Keep moving forward."

Next, we saw a large, beautiful tree in all of its glorious fall color, growing out of a solid rock -limestone. Another message. "You are strong. You are rooted well. Continue to reach for the sky even when circumstances seem unlikely. You can and will grow."

Imagine then the space—glass surrounding—opening your ability to see outward, to appreciate beauty, to see beyond. Honestly, such extraordinary gifts. The universe (well, and probably the Gaylord), also provided a little guy painting right outside the window where we were presenting the Forum. I loved it! I told the attendees that if all went to hell, we could watch the paint dry. I have such new value for the mundane.

The Forum went in a direction that I was not expecting. One of the first requests that arose when I asked what people were looking to gain from the Forum was a request for a conversation about vulnerability. Is there a place for vulnerability in leadership?

Oh Jeez.

This message of vulnerability was one that kept recurring. The week before attending the Forum, we delivered a webinar on *"Engaging Men in the Conversation."* Patrick Burke and Lynn Hoffman, both leaders of Aon, talked about vulnerability.

On Saturday before the Forum, I decided to have my hair colored. I don't have the confidence yet to go without my wig. My hair, now coming in completely white, exposed white sideburns beneath my blonde wig. I look to Lizzy (my daughter) for the truth about personal maintenance. She told me she thought I probably should consider color.

I've not been to the salon in ten months. The woman who previously took care of my hair is out on maternity leave. I talked with the salon owner, who agreed, with hesitance, to put color on. Since I've had chemo, there's some question about hair color.

The salon owner did not have time to wash out the color, so he directed me to another young man who would finish my process. The young man was Sean, and I must admit, I was battling some of my own unconscious bias when I saw him. Sean is a very petite man with coal black hair. The left side of his head is completely shaved. He had a highly puffed-up, comb-over, pure white, and angled in four separate spikes toward his eyes. Black eyeliner lined his upper and lower lid. As he approached the chair I was sitting in, I could feel the pace of my breath increasing. I love artists. I love funky. I love funky artists. I think, however, that I don't so much love funky artists working on what little hair **I have** on *my head*. Absolutely would support them working on others.

As Sean and I exchanged nice-ities, I realized he was a very kind soul. I asked him how long he thought it would be before I could go without my wig altogether. I told him I spoke professionally as part of my work, and that I did not want people gazing back at me thinking, "Oh that poor soul, she has cancer."

Sean asked me what I spoke about. I told him that I spoke on leadership. Then, the most extraordinary thing came out of this funky, incredibly wise, artist. He said, "Well, isn't true leadership about courage, confidence, authenticity, vulnerability? My favorite speakers and leaders have been those who have been willing to share their personal stories, who are vulnerable, those who don't try to be anyone beyond who they really are!"

Oh Jeez. Seriously? In the middle of getting my hair colored, I have to have a life lesson? The answer is yes. In the middle of whatever, there is opportunity for a significant life lesson. Sean had no idea about the wisdom he had just offered. He spoke to me at both head and heart level. Here's a kid living his own message. I knew what I needed to do.

The Forum went on very well throughout the day. Just before closing, I had a 30-minute slot for a presentation. Because Nashville is the Music City, the theme was, *"Conducting Beyond Limits—Leadership Lessons for Leveraging Inclusion."* My piece was called "Orchestrating Your Plan" and was a focus on personal and professional takeaways from the day.

In researching what goes into producing music, I found that there are eight steps. I focused on three: writing the song, over-dubbing, which is bringing your "sweetness" to the music, and mastering. In mastering, I circled back to the initial conversation about vulnerability in leadership. Then, I took my wig off. I told my story. I was terrified. Shock and awe enveloped the room. There I was, standing before these people, bald like an eagle, and really letting them in. My point: you never really know who stands in front of you. All of us are battling something . . . all of us! And rather than judge, what if we all helped each other just be . . . What if we **encouraged** the possibility of just be-ing? I cried as I spoke— also really tough, and I told them that I would not apologize for my tears, that I *was not/am not* a victim, that this is a condition of my lived experience, and that it was OK, that I am OK.

On November 18, I have my next scans. As you can imagine, I'm scared and anxious to get my next "ticket" to pass go, to live on, to be vulnerable. I have appreciated and valued each one of you on this journey, and I'm asking again for you to storm heaven with prayers for a clean scan, for continued healing and wholeness, and for an increased knowingness that just as I am, I am enough.

TEST RESULTS...MORE TESTS ARE NEEDED

Journal Entry by Maureen O'Brien
November 16, 2016

Hello Prayer Warriors!

Well, I got the results from my CT Scan as well as the nuclear full body bone scan. (That just sounds awful, right?) The CT scan was good, the bone scan raised some questions.

When I received the results at 5 a.m. on Monday, I was a basket case. The results came through MyChart, directly into my inbox. Terrifying to read words that I do not understand. You may be thinking to yourself, "why did you open the email?" Test results are very seductive...you want to know...and you don't want to know.

This morning, at 7a.m., I had a PET Scan. I have an appointment with my doctor on Friday at 1 p.m. Would so very much appreciate your prayers.

GOT MY NEXT TICKET!!!! I AM OKAY! THANK YOU AND THANK GOD!

Journal Entry by Maureen O'Brien
November 17, 2016

HELLO PRAYER WARRIORS!

I just received a call from my wonderful primary doctor, Terry West. He asked how I was doing. I told him while still holding my breath, that I hoped HE would be able to tell me that I was doing great. He said, "I *am* able to tell you that!"

This morning, and again at 5 a.m., my cell phone indicated there was a message. Sure enough, a message from MyChart. My heart raced. I considered what to do next. I deleted the message without opening it. I have an appointment with my Oncologist tomorrow (Friday) at 1 p.m. I decided that I needed to just wait and get the news in person so that there'd be no confusion about what I was reading.

So incredibly hard to do. Wait. Wonder. The message in the phone . . . continuously seducing you. Take a look.

I got up and showered and started my day. While loading my car, the beautiful and unbelievably kind Polly Ernzen walked by my house. She entered my driveway when she saw me and just gave me a hug. I wept and told her that I really hoped I would be OK.

This morning I was siding lady— measuring a couple of siding/window jobs. While on a job with Wesley, my foreman, the homeowner that we were working with said, "look...there's a rainbow...a sun dog in the sky." I could feel myself ready to weep. Could this be Mom and Dad letting me know all was well? Could they be telling me that I need not worry any longer, that I could finally exhale? I said to the homeowner that that rainbow was from my Dad!

Following those proposals, I flipped my hat and proceeded to the Global office to be CEO of the Global Women's Leadership Forum. I got a text from my sister Patricia asking me how the PET Scan went. I told her that the scan went fine, that the results were in my inbox, but that I wasn't going to look. Patricia has her PhD in nursing and is the Associate Dean of Nursing at the University of Kentucky. She's our family medical expert and is the go-to person when anyone's health is an issue.

A few minutes went by, and another text arrived from Patricia. "The PET Scan results are not in your MyChart. It's your glucose test results. Your glucose is fine."

Oh jeez. I've been fretting this all day and only now do I understand that the results *never were* in my Inbox.

A few more minutes passed, and my cell phone rang. My Primary Care Doc's number surfaced as the caller. My heart started to pound. Nicole, the Wonder Woman and my right arm, was in my office. She just smiled and said, "You got this! Answer the call."

And there it was. The answer I had prayed for. The answer I know that YOU prayed for. I got my next ticket to go on with life! While I don't know the duration of this ticket (I'll learn that tomorrow), for now I am just so very grateful! I can never thank you enough for being the warrior for me that you are! I COULD FEEL YOUR PRAYERS~! My heart is full. I love you to the moon . . .

Love you so very, very much!
MO

CHAPTER 26

MEREDITH OGBURN MAHEU, ONCOLOGY NURSE

Hand holder. Voice of advocacy. Fearless. That's what I can tell you about Meredith. Prior to chemo, I had to have intrathecal therapy—an injection of chemotherapy into the spine. I was terrified, even though I had done this once before. The first time, I was put to sleep (or I was so sick I simply don't remember it). The next time, however, things didn't go as planned, and it was Meredith who stepped in and created a more bearable situation for me. I knew she was **"partnering in the fight"** *as my advocate.*

It's critically important to have advocates on your healthcare team. They must see you—really see you—and be your voice when you are not able. I was so incredibly fortunate to have these angels in scrubs as part of my community of care.

Let me begin with who I am and how I came to know Mo. I have been a nurse for fifteen years. I have provided care in many different areas. The longest part of my career has been caring for patients with cancer, both as a hospital-based nurse and as an educator for nurses who provide care to cancer patients. I am one of the hospital nurses who was fortunate enough to care for Mo during her treatment. I truly feel that I was blessed to be able to provide care for her and be on this journey to remission with her. I'll tell you more about why I feel this way in a bit.

When a nurse is asked why they became a nurse, the answer is almost universally the same: "I want to help people." This sentiment is the same for me. Nurses don't go into nursing for the glamor, the money, or the prestige. We genuinely want to help people. We see people on their best days, worst days, first days, and, unfortunately, their last days. We celebrate with our patients, we comfort our patients, and we cry for our patients. Every nurse can recall those special patients who made an impact on their career. Maybe it was because we were heartbroken when we held their hand as they passed, or maybe it was because their light shone so brightly that it couldn't be extinguished. Mo was one of the patients that I will never forget because of how brightly her light shines.

> EVERY NURSE CAN RECALL THOSE
> SPECIAL PATIENTS WHO MADE AN
> IMPACT ON THEIR CAREER.

I still remember Mo's first course of chemotherapy. Her first cycle was rough. When a patient gets a cancer diagnosis, the goal is to begin treatment as quickly as possible to stop the disease progression. Mo's oncologist held this philosophy: "When my patient *really* wants to fight the disease, I'm going to do everything I can to cure the cancer."

That fight included throwing everything but the kitchen sink at Maureen that first cycle. She had several procedures, and I could see she was exhausted and didn't know what was going to happen next. But even through that tough cycle, I could see she was willing to fight. We as health professionals united. We all fought with her.

She showed her desire to fight in many ways. The one that stands out so much to me is her desire to be a partner in her fight. She didn't want to sit back, take her medications, and simply do as she was told. She wanted to understand the next steps. She wanted to be part of the decisions. She wanted to know the plan. And my favorite thing was that she wanted to know what she could do to help the plan. Having a patient wanting to be a partner made us not want to let her down. It made us feel like we were part of a relay race and she was the anchor of the team. When we symbolically handed her the baton, she took it and brought us home for the win.

Now, it wasn't just Mo who was a partner in her treatment plan. She also had an unbelievably supportive community of care full of family and friends. Since her treatment happened before COVID-19, she was able to have as many visitors as she wanted. Her family and friends lifted her spirits when they were low. They brought her items to make her stay easier. Most importantly, they brought her support. They acted as advocates when she wasn't feeling well. They also acted as resources, asking questions for her when she didn't remember she wanted to ask a specific question. And they did all of this while showing respect for everyone they encountered.

Respect is something not always shown to nurses. Nurses can often be verbally and physically abused by patients and their family members. Sometimes, nurses are treated like waitresses and given orders by patients instead of requests. There have been times when I've wanted to tell a patient, "I'm so sorry I was late with your lunch. My patient in another hall was having a stroke, which kind of required all my focus. But hey, here's your soup." Instead, we simply apologize, take the comments, and maybe offer to get a new tray. I tell you this to highlight the stark difference in caring for Mo.

Mo and her tribe showed respect in so many ways. The first thing Mo did was make sure she knew the names of her nurses and her nurses' aides, and her family and other community members did the same. This may seem like a little thing, but I will tell you that being greeted by name really helps a nurse feel more connected to their patient. The next thing was something that always struck me when I cared for her. Whenever I would come into her room, she would stop what she was doing to give her full attention to me. For me, it was a sign that she respected me and my time. Again, her tribe did the exact same thing. Whenever I would enter her room, even if they were involved in a discussion, they would pause and turn their attention to me.

BEING GREETED BY NAME REALLY HELPS
A NURSE FEEL MORE CONNECTED TO
THEIR PATIENT.

Did I provide Mo with different care because of the respect she showed me as compared to what I provided other patients? Probably not. At least I hope not. I like to think that I provide every patient with excellent care. The difference is, I wanted to simply spend time getting to know Mo because of how she treated me. I planned my shifts around her. I didn't want to be late with other patients because I was spending time with her, so I would plan my rounds in a way that ensured I could see her and spend a few extra minutes with her. I remembered things about her previous hospitalizations that helped me in her care for her next hospitalization. I remembered how she responded to medications. I remembered how she looked from prior hospitalizations and could compare that to how she looked during her next hospitalization. This bit of perspective made it easier for me to speak up and advocate for her.

WHILE ADVOCATING FOR A PATIENT IS A ROUTINE PART OF A SHIFT FOR A NURSE, FOR A PATIENT, IT CAN MAKE ALL THE DIFFERENCE.

One specific time that I was able to advocate for Mo was during a procedure called intrathecal chemotherapy, where she would get an injection of chemotherapy into her spine. This is a stressful procedure for a patient since they must lie perfectly still in uncomfortable positions. The patients are also awake during the procedure, so they feel *everything*. I went with Mo to the procedure to monitor the chemotherapy being infused. She lay facedown on the table, her spine facing the physician. During the procedure, I could see that she was in an inordinate amount of pain. Mo tried to tell the physician of her discomfort, but he dismissed her and told her it would be over soon. She wanted the procedure to continue, so she remained quiet. As Mo's nurse, I had to advocate for her. I held her hand so she could squeeze it as hard as she needed. Then, I spoke up and told the doctor she was in a lot of pain. When I advocated for her, the physician listened. He was able to understand how much pain Mo was in, and he made the necessary changes to make it less uncomfortable for her. While advocating for a patient is a routine part of a shift for a nurse, for a patient, it can make all the difference.

When Mo was discharged from the hospital, I knew she would be well cared for because I had observed how attentive her tribe was during her hospitalizations. But after cancer patients are discharged from the hospital, that usually means the end of the journey for the nurses. With other patients, I would worry about how they were doing when they got home. Since we don't typically hear updates on how patients are doing, we are left in the dark. Of course we are invested in our patient's recovery and want to see them win their fight with cancer, but often, we simply don't know the end of the story.

With Mo, I had the awesome experience of getting to find out about her fight. She came by the hospital, thanked the nurses that had cared for her, and updated us on her progress. It was wonderful to celebrate with her when she was first told she was in remission. Mo made sure to show me that she knew I had made an impact on her fight. She did that by letting me know she was in remission.

When I started this passage, I said I felt fortunate and blessed to have been Mo's nurse during her cancer treatment. The reasons I feel blessed begin with the respect she showed me and my colleagues. That respect is something I am grateful for and will never forget. I was also fortunate to feel like I was her partner and not a caretaker. Finding out that my hard work helped her achieve remission will always be with me.

There are times when I wonder if I should continue to be a nurse, days when I want to quit for one reason or another. Then I think about Mo. I remember that I made an impact on her. I made a difference in her life. I was appreciated by her. I was appreciated by her tribe. These thoughts give me the strength to continue to be the best nurse, advocate, and caregiver that I can be. It helps me to remember that we're all on the same team and we're here to fight on!

ILLUMINATIONS

Family members of patients going through cancer treatment often ask what they should do to care for their loved one, and I often recommended spending time with the patient. For example, when a patient is in the hospital getting treatment, they aren't alone. They have nurses and aides to help with everything they need. However, when they are discharged, they don't have those nurses and aides. Patients are exhausted, and sometimes just getting out of bed to go to the bathroom is exhausting. Instead of taking all their time off to spend with a loved one in the hospital, perhaps a more meaningful opportunity for family members to offer support is to use some of that time to help after the patient has been discharged home.

Another important thing family and friends can do is voice any concerns about the discharge home to someone on the medical team. Health care providers will never know everything about their patients, and the more information we receive, the better we can plan for extended help. If there is a financial concern about affording medications or treatments, tell us. If there is a concern about the patient sharing a bathroom with their young children, tell us. If there is a concern that the patient is becoming depressed about their disease, tell us. When we have that information, we can and will use it to help in any way we can.

BLESSINGS, BLESSINGS OF THE SEASON!

Journal Entry by Maureen O'Brien

December 4, 2016

Blessings to all of you! The last couple of weeks have been incredibly tough. In my last post, I told you I had gotten the news that all was well. It is, and it took awhile to get absolute confirmation.

When I went to see my doctor here in the suburbs on November 18 to review my PET Scan, she said it looked good but that she wanted me to have additional tests. She said that I needed another CT of my skull and an MRI of my shoulder because both showed some question marks in the nuclear bone scan. She went on to say that since my shoulder had "lit up" in the PET, it was possible that I would need to have radiation on my shoulder, something that was discussed from the beginning. Dan and I were to leave for Florida on Sunday, November 20 to spend the week of Thanksgiving in the sunshine. She invited that I go immediately and have the tests before we left for our trip.

I thought for a moment. I told her I wasn't going to do it. I already had a date scheduled with the doctors at the University of Chicago Hospital on November 28. I told her I had to have a break, that I was going to go to Florida and enjoy the week. I told her I would do nothing until I had the meeting with them. I think she was quite surprised. Frankly, I surprised myself.

The week in Florida was amazing. Dan, Lizzy, and I went to a different beach everyday. The weather was magnificent, soothing, and a calming relief. While I missed the boys terribly, we planned our return for Saturday, November 26, and we intended to gather as family for a Thanksgiving Brunch at our house on Sunday, November 27.

Amy, my granddaughter, at age two, brings magical joy and leaves a trail! We had a good meal together with lots of laughter. Then we began dragging all of the Christmas decorations out of the basement. Usually, this is a job I do by myself. Not possible now. The house began to awaken in holiday splendor. I do love this time of year.

On Monday morning, Dan and I rose early for our trip to Chicago. We had cds and paper copy reports of all scans in tow. I was scared. I started thinking about possible surgery on my shoulder, the possibility of radiation, all the what ifs?!

Dr. Sonali Smith is a lymphoma guru and has been part of my team since the beginning. She was my "second opinion," but the facts are, she determined my protocol and she and Dr. Bayer (my original doc before he got moved to DeKalb when Northwestern acquired Kishwaukee Hospital after round 2 of my chemo—ugh!) worked closely together to get me well. I had seen Dr. Smith in July once it was determined I was in remission. I intended to now become her full time patient.

Dr. Godfrey, the Research Fellow that works with Dr. Smith, came in first. He was beaming!

"Your PET looks great! Your blood work looks great! How do you feel?"

"I feel scared," I said. It seems like there are still some questions. Do you think I need radiation?"

His reaction was stunning. Imagine hitting someone in the face with a wet sponge. You know how their face squinches up and their eyes close tight? They kind of back up from the force of the hit? That was his reaction.

"Why would you have radiation? Your'e in remission! We don't radiate people who are cancer free!"

Yep. You guessed it. I burst into tears. Relief.

He went on to say, "your shoulder lit up with new activity because new bone is growing there! We WANT that to happen. Your hip lit up because you have a metal rod in it! It's ALWAYS going to light up. You're doing GREAT! You need to live your life!"

At that point, Dr. Smith walked into the room. She too said that all was amazingly well. She told me that I looked great, that if she didn't know better, she would never know I had been so ill. She turned to Dr. Godfrey and told him that when she met me the first time, I was unresponsive...that she wanted to admit me that very day, something of which I have no recollection. She told me that I should come back at the end of March. At that time, I'll need a blood test and an appointment with her to see how I'm feeling. That's it. No drama. No more tests. Nada.

I hugged both she and Dr. Godfrey. Again, so relieved and grateful.

Then we went on to see the orthopedic oncologist, Dr. Luu. I'd need to have several Xrays on my shoulder and my hip so that he could see what was happening. He first wanted to see what movement I had with my arm. I was scared. I thought it should be better by now. He was elated by what I could do!

We took the Xrays. Dr. Luu came beaming and bounding into the room. He put the Xrays up on the screen. "Your shoulder is healed," he said. "What you need now is physical therapy. I'll write the order."

Unbelievable. Bones don't usually heal in chemotherapy. Chemotherapy is meant to kill cells—including those that are trying to grow new bones. Truly a miracle!

I remember sitting there, breathless, unbelieving. Ten days ago, in another doctor's office, all I could think about was a surgery, radiation, endless tests. Now, the next thing is physical therapy? I am so incredibly grateful. He wrote the order and told me to come back and see him for a checkup in six months.

Again, your prayers have lifted us. I am so grateful to each and every one of you for carrying me when I was not able to carry myself! I want to share with you a letter that Dan wrote to his colleagues last week after we got the news. I also want to wish you the happiest and most blessed of holidays. We certainly will celebrate one! I still am intending to have my brunch. I obviously didn't do it today. Couldn't. I'm now thinking about January 2 from noon - 3 p.m. It's a Monday, but a holiday for most. Would that work for you? Could you please respond here and let me know? Honestly, if you're reading this, I want you to come!

We love you. We're grateful for you. We wish you an absolutely magical holiday season!

Here's Dan's letter to his workmates last week. It articulates well what our family holds in our heart:

In February, my wife, Maureen, was diagnosed with Stage IV lymphoma, a cancer of the blood that eroded her bones. It was the most aggressive lymphoma that her doctors had seen, there is no stage 5. Before she could begin chemo, a rod was placed in her hip to strengthen the weakened bone. Her shoulder also needed a rod as it already had a fracture on the head of the arm bone.

Normally, chemo would begin 30 days after a surgery. The cancer was so advanced and aggressive that it was decided to begin chemo after 21 days. There would be no time to fix the shoulder. In the first round of chemo, the doctors struggled to treat the normal side effects. Her temperature would swing from 103 to 95 within an hour. Tests turned up the flu virus and indications of pneumonia (Get a flu shot.) The pneumonia never developed but she had to go through the first round of chemo with the flu. I had never seen "rigors" before. Rigors happened when the body tries hard to create heat to fuel a fever. The whole body shivers. Huge, full body shivers.

Da Bride was still weak from the flu when it was time to begin the second round of chemo. Her doctors reduced the dosage to 75%. Her chemo was administered continuously in a hospital for 5 days. 6 rounds, one every 3 weeks. Round 6 completed July 8.

Blood tests in July, August, and November have revealed no evidence of cancer. PET scans in July and November reveal no signs of the disease. X-rays of her shoulder in November revealed that it had healed on its own. Chemo is designed to kill new cells and those in formation so it was very gratifying to see the new bone in the fracture area. Next appointments are in the 4-6 month time frame to monitor continued remission.

Early this year I shared our news with you and asked to be included in your prayers. Da Bride and I have another request. If you asked anything of the Lord on our

behalf, please thank Him on our behalf. We would like to be in the company of the one leper who returned to give thanks rather than in the company of the 9 who did not. Please thank Him. We are so grateful. There is not enough prayer in the world. Thank you, thank you, thank you, ...
Gracias a Dios!

DanO

CONNECTING WITH THE DAUGHTER OF AN ANGEL!

Journal Entry by Maureen O'Brien

December 12, 2016

Dan and I are in Florida at Camp Global, our oasis. Camp Global is in Trinity, FL and was originally the villa owned by my Mom and Dad. We bought it when they moved to Milwaukee. I can feel them here. It still smells like my Mom when I walk in the door.

It has been bittersweet being here this week. We are renting the villa to a couple from Missouri through mid-April. They are friends of one of our neighbors here. This is something we've not done before. When I was so sick, it made a lot of sense. We didn't think we'd be able to come this winter. Since Mom's passing on September 19, I have been desperate to feel a sense of her. I feel her here. It'll be incredibly hard to leave on Thursday when the renters arrive.

One of the gifts of this trip has been that I finally got to meet Gina, the daughter of Rosemary, who was part of my "wisdom tribe" here. Rosemary lived across the street. She and I shopped frequently, shared much laughter and some tears. Last year, Rosemary had a recurrence of leukemia, something she had battled 15 years ago and had been cancer free until last year. Rosemary lost her fight, joining the angels. She left the world before learning of my illness, but I have felt her presence throughout this journey, both in the silence and through her daughter, Gina.

I never met Gina until yesterday, but she has been an active cheerleader, encourager, and inspirer here on this site. She has been rooting for me to win this battle from the beginning, and I have so appreciated it. We had the pleasure of also meeting Gina's husband Brian. He's a blast. Gina is the image of her Mom, and we spent a good deal of time simply sharing stories. Such a gift.

I am so cognizant that the true gifts of this season are the people who have had impact; those who are here, and those who have passed on. My hope for all of us is that we spend some significant time reflecting on those people, those gifts. The wrappings, the glitter, the tinsel, the lights . . . all get packed away, but our memories linger on.

Know that I consider YOU gift of my life. I am blessed. I am grateful.

CALLING ALL PRAYER WARRIORS—
ANXIOUS FOR MY NEXT TICKET—VOLUME II

Journal Entry by Maureen O'Brien
March 22, 2017

Hello Dear Ones!

Does it feel as though I'm always asking? It must. Well, here I am again!

Tomorrow I will see Dr. Sonoli Smith to get my stamp on my next four month "ticket." I feel good. I've been working hard in physical therapy and have gained much strength in my left arm. My foot drop is less noticeable, and overall, I'm moving in a good direction.

On Wednesday of last week, I had my annual mammogram. Saturday, via email (through MyChart—which frankly, I'm starting to HATE), I learned that there were some suspicious calcifications which needed additional viewing. I went in on Monday and learned that I need to have a biopsy. That will happen this Friday.

Friends, I'm asking once again that you storm heaven. I don't know why this is happening. Gotta say, I'm kinda mad at God. Not sure why, after all I've been through, this is necessary. I know God is big enough to handle my mad, AND it's still hard.

Here's what I know for sure: 90% of calcifications are benign. Even if what I have is SOMETHING...it'd be DCIS, Stage 0 breast cancer. Treatment would be a lumpectomy and radiation. No chemo.

Even knowing that, as you can imagine, I feel an interesting amount of anxiety. I'm just mad...and this mad shows up with a lot of tears.

It is interesting, though, how God keeps presenting in my life even when I work hard to push Him out. Today, I met Aggie Mc-Duffee (you just have to love her because of her name). Aggie is probably in her late 70s or early 80s. She's incredibly beautiful with a southern drawl which just melts your sweet 'lil ole heart! She was a realtor for her entire life. Now, her primary job is caring for her husband who is dying, AND he has Alzheimer's. Aggie has had a difficult life which includes a pretty ugly divorce from her first husband, and then suddenly losing one of her adult children seven years ago. Aggie shared much with me in the period of about an hour at her kitchen table. I was actually there to sell her soffit and fascia, which by the way, I did sell. Biggest soffit job I've ever gotten in the 30 years I've been in business. I think we can all agree that the reason that I was *really* there had nothing to do with selling building products!

I too shared with Aggie. I told her my story. Cried. Cried in front of a complete stranger. And I was safe. I told her that I was so mad. My two sisters, my sister-in-law, Lizzy, Britta and I had plans to go to the Kohler Spa this weekend to celebrate my good health. With this news, that all had to be cancelled. Aggie just nodded. She affirmed that God was big enough to handle my mad! Then she told me that she'd pray for me, that with God, mad and all, I was strong enough to handle whatever the next step is, that we'd get through it together, and that she'd be part of my team too!

Aggie McDuffee. Yet another angel on earth. Showing up just when I need her.

Of course, I am hoping, praying, trusting... that this biopsy is nothing more than a nuisance. I am praying that on Tuesday I get word that the calcifications are benign. And once again, I'm asking you. Please pray that whatever the outcome, I handle it with peace and trust. And while you're already in prayer, would you remember my new friend Aggie McDuffee?

Thanks in advance for storming heaven!

IT. IS. BENIGN!

Journal Entry by Maureen O'Brien

March 28, 2017

My Dearest Prayer Warriors!

Thank you. From the bottom of my heart, thank you. Once again, you stormed the heavens. Prayers were answered. IT. WAS. BENIGN!

We're planning a big trip to Europe this summer. My Healing Tour. Dan and I will celebrate our 35th wedding anniversary. Now that I have my "ticket stamped," we have much to celebrate, and we are grateful.

Thank you for being in our lives. Thank you for surrounding us with love, light, and hope. Thank you for answering when we call, and for always holding us up. We are grateful.

Much, much love~

MO

THE EVE OF THE BIG TEST

Journal Entry by Maureen O'Brien

July 19, 2017

Here I am again...asking. Tomorrow I have my PET Scan. It is one year to the day that I heard the words, "You are in remission." I'm hanging on to those words, and praying I'll hear them again tomorrow. What I'm asking is that you storm heaven, making the same ask.

Cancer sucks. It causes this incredible confusion that creates a tug of war between your logical brain and your crazy brain. My logical brain tells me there is no reason to believe that I am anything but healed. I feel good. I am so much stronger. All that weight I lost...well, it has not been lost for long. I found every bit of it, which my doctor tells me is a good thing?!? *Losing weight* is a bigger issue with cancer.

My crazy brain creates its own stories. It nudges and whispers things like, "you didn't know you were sick the last time," or "there were no signs," or "what makes you think you deserve to pass go on this?"

My friend Tom told me to put a rubber band on my wrist and every time I start to tell myself a story, to snap it. Great idea. I've done it. Now I'll go into the test tomorrow with a black and blue wrist. Clearly, I'm doing a lot of storytelling. That's what cancer does.

You have always held me up, and I need you again now. I need your prayers for peace. Peace that I'm able to get through the test which requires the injection of a radioactive dye throughout my entire system. One hour following the injection, I'll spend 45 minutes in a machine which will scan my entire body. While not completely enclosed, it feels awfully tight to a person who is claustrophobic.

I need your prayers for peace. I need your prayers to trust that I am fully healed; that all is well. You have held me up on every step of this journey, and I'm asking again. Will you storm heaven?

Thanks in advance. I love you. I hope to share continued good news following the test tomorrow.

I ASKED THAT YOU STORM HEAVEN...
AND YOU DID!

Journal Entry by Maureen O'Brien

July 20, 2017

We are beyond grateful. Today, after a tough start (they tried seven times to start my IV), I now have a black and blue hand and fore-arm to match my black and blue wrist. But it's ok. At 3:45 pm. I heard the words I longed to hear. I AM CANCER FREE! No tests until December. And then, only a blood test!

I cannot even begin to express the feelings I hold in my heart. Thank you for your prayers. Thank you for your support. Thank you for your unrelenting belief that we could fight...and with God's help and your prayers, we could win!

I ask that you return to prayer in thanksgiving for this gift. I also ask that you send up a prayer for Dan, who has never wa-vered, who had offered unending strength, and who has been my ROCK throughout this tumultuous time.

I am so very blessed. Thank you for blessing me with the gift of YOU in my life! I love you.

CONCLUSION

Reflecting on this time in my life—and, frankly, reading this collective myself—has been incredibly tough. As days turn to seasons and seasons to years, there are some things that I have forgotten. Reading the words has been like reliving them, but these pages have helped me gain clarity about things.

Whatever news you're getting, remember that your story is not *my* story or anyone else's. Take the information as it comes one day at a time (or sometimes half day at a time) the best that you can. Let tears come, but also look, really *look*, for the goodness and gifts of every circumstance. Pay attention.

Speaking of paying attention, I believe there are mini-miracles—signs that happen to us, for us, every day—but we're so busy with our heads down that we miss them. Here's one I remember clearly:

I had finished my last round of chemo and was waiting to go for my final PET scan. Dan and I decided to go to a prayer service at our church. When we left the service, we took a short drive to see the sunset. On the drive, the radio was playing the song "Tell Your Heart to Beat Again" by Danny Gokey. After listening to the lyrics, I knew the song was a direct message to me. I was *certain* of it. Hearing that song, I absolutely knew I was going to be okay.

Now that I've had this time to reflect on my own journey from a place of health, gratitude, and love, I want to offer you the following advice:

Recognize that each life has some rainfall. Without the cloudy days, we would not have the same appreciation for the sunny ones. Force yourself to take a walk each day, even if that only means a couple of steps with a walker. Do what you can to get yourself upright.

Tell the people in your life that they matter. Let them know every day. If you've had some hiccups in relationships, fix them now. In the long run, none of those things are going to matter.

Do the best that you can every day. Eat well. Care for your body, even if that means eating chocolate peanut butter ice cream with your sister-in-law in the middle of the night.

Believe in something bigger than yourself. It doesn't matter what you call it—it could be God, the universe, or whatever—but *believe*. It will help you and your community get through the darkest nights, even if they happen in the middle of the day.

Gratitude. Practice it. No matter the circumstance you're in, try to be grateful, even if it's only for your perfect shade of red lipstick or the silk scarf for your missing hair.

Know that every drop of medicine will reach its intended cell. Believe. Believe. *Believe.*

Bring joy wherever you can—this is a choice. And keep lookin' up!

If this book meant something to you or a loved one, please consider leaving a review with the bookseller of your choice. All proceeds from this book after production costs will be donated to cancer research and patient care, and your honest feedback can help others who may also be looking for comfort during a difficult time.

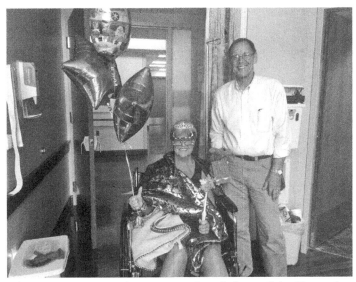

The Last Day! Mo and Dan Being Paraded out of the Hospital

Mo and Daughter Lizzy

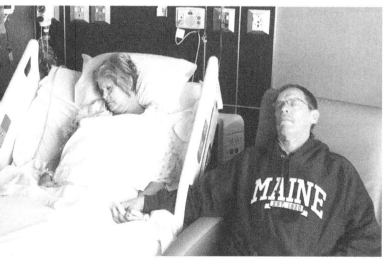

Mo and Dan—First Round of Chemo

Tears of Joy—
Britta and Mo
Celebrating Remission!

Mo and Elizabeth
Green—Five
Years in Remission
Party for
#26PointsOfLight

The Garden Angels. SITTING: *Britta McKenna, Cheryl Whitten, Diane Wolf.* STANDING: *Geary Wolf, Melanie Ley, Sharon Mitchell, Vicki Grochowski, Debbie Rosso, Jeri Gosselin, Jennifer Smith, Susan Romano, Joe (Donchaknow) Romano, Susan Fencl.* MISSING FROM PHOTO: *Mariann Schira, Lynn Ducar, Terri Hoehne, Deb McGrath, Laurel Flinn*

Mo and Siblings: First Post-Chemo Gathering. Left to right: Mo, Bill, Patricia, Karen

ACKNOWLEDGMENTS

As you might imagine, for all of us, this book was challenging to write. It was a true labor of love. It was hard to relive the months of what felt like real darkness. But in that darkness, there was also so much light. So many blessings. And so much to share with you today.

Knowing this would be a tough and emotional project, we needed a great editor to help us put this into logical and readable form for you, the reader. We owe tremendous gratitude to Sarah Kolb-Williams, our editor, project manager, and all-around Director of Everything! This book would not be in your hands without her magic touch.

Speaking of magic touch, we have Athena Currier to thank for this book's incredible design. She brought my words and my vision to life in a way I never imagined possible—thank you, thank you, thank you!

Thank you to Sean Gallagher for giving freely of his time and contributing the foreword to this book.

And thank you to you, reader, for sharing this journey with us. Know that we're sending you love, hope, and light, whatever your journey ahead.

RESOURCES

For additional information and support, try the following worthy organizations (or visit https://www.globalwlf.com for more ideas on how to give, share, and connect):

CaringBridge	https://www.caringbridge.org/
Leukemia and Lymphoma Society	https://www.lls.org
Leukemia Research Foundation	https://www.allbloodcancers.org
Lymphoma Research Foundation	https://www.lymphoma.org
MealTrain	https://www.mealtrain.com

ABOUT THE AUTHOR

Maureen O'Brien is a business speaker, author, community leader, and cancer survivor. Armed with a degree in education and the equivalent of a PhD in hard knocks—and now five years in remission—Maureen uses her experience to encourage and inspire others who may feel hopeless in the face of new challenges.

Named "One of the Most Powerful and Influential Women in Illinois" by the National Diversity Council, O'Brien is a renowned expert in Strategic Thinking, Leadership Development, and Relationship Selling. She is a recipient of the Dr. MLK Award for the Acceleration of Women in Leadership by the Illinois Commission on Diversity and Human Relations and a renowned expert in diversity, equity, and inclusion with an emphasis on the advocacy of women in the workplace.

O'Brien is the author of *Get your Big Girl Pants on and SELL Something: A Handbook for Women (and Really Progressive Men) In Sales* and *Oneness. Wellness. Wholeness: 4 Ways to*

TakeCara U! She has also published a children's book, *And the Children Watched: A Reflection on the COVID-19 Pandemic.* She is a mother of four and grandmother of four, and she lives in Illinois with her husband.

Maureen O'Brien battled stage 4 lymphoma . . . and won.

The title of my next book is *With the Time We Have Left*. Each of us has a finite amount of time here on the planet, and this book will offer words of encouragement for this journey we all share.

For now, I want to leave you with this question: What will *you* do with the time you have left?

Made in the USA
Middletown, DE
08 October 2022